The Lunatic Gene

How To Make Sense of Your Life

By

Adam Shaw

The Heart Guy

The Lunatic Gene

Have you ever wondered what your future holds?

By talking this through with those who have had weeks, days, hours or even minutes to live, it swiftly becomes clear that most people live their lives stuck in a rut, doing things they don't really want to do, with people they would rather not be with, for reasons they cannot properly explain or justify. This can lead to a lot of pain when imminent death becomes a reality and the wake-up call arrives – too late to do anything about it.

Your time is your most valuable asset

If you wake up every day filled with joy, and happily embracing whatever life throws at you, the odds are you do not need to read this book. If, however, you don't love your life, frequently feel depressed or low, are stuck in a job or relationship that you hate, or have even felt suicidal, then it is likely you have the negative manifestation of The Lunatic Gene.

This book will explain this phenomenon, what you can do to stop fighting your Lunatic Gene, and start dancing with it

By the end of this book, you will understand that you already have The Lunatic Gene, and are living in a lunatic asylum. It is a guide to the early warning symptoms of serious illness, and what you can do about it now to start feeling happier about you and your life.

Adam Shaw - The Heart Guy

www.thelunaticgene.com

Acknowledgements

"It's only fair that I thank a few people who have been pivotal in the process of getting this to print.

To the team who gave their time and energy reading through my script and giving me feedback, I could not have done this without you. Michael Page, Susan Kybett, Alan Sharland, Chris Sauerwein, Pam Lawrence and Bruce King, your selfless time investment, feedback and support is much appreciated. To Jackie and David Ford who helped me bring this book to life on Amazon.

To my friend/coach/partner in crime, Bobby Gill, for your subtle persuasiveness that led me to progressing this venture over the final line. Thank you for the most fun kick up the backside I've ever had! To Fiona Maguire and Sidra Jafri, thank you for your friendship and for helping me out of some of my darkest places.

To all of my family, you have all been phenomenal in supporting me through this journey, and providing much of the background for this book. I could not have done this without you.

To all those who challenged me, thank you for helping me to find my voice.

Mike Howley - you are a star. The regular calls, laughs and throwaway quotes have been an essential part of this journey. Jackie Jenks, thank you for your guidance along this path: the support you have provided has been pivotal. To my friends, teachers and mentors, Art Giser and Anne Jirsch for your fun and open teaching styles which have taught me so much. To my teachers David Shephard, Christian Pankhurst, Dr Bernie Siegel, Dr John DeMartini, and Dr Jerry Jampolsky, for the key lessons you have all given me.

Finally, to my friend Lord David Evans, who helped me when I was most lost on my entrepreneurial journey, and taught me how to make a business work.

I love you all."

Adam

Testimonials

"Adam Shaw - The Heart Guy - has written a book that will make you think deeply about what is important in your life and, even more so, to feel what is important in your life. Mixing depressing stories of regret, from those he nursed through their last days of life, with laugh-out-loud anecdotes and one-liners from his own 'lunatic' life experiences he challenges the reader to consider, far in advance of their own demise, the questions many only consider on their death-beds - and find difficult to answer. Giving us a head-start on many who die wondering what their lives could have been like 'if only...' he shows how modern medicine, dealing only with the physical aspects of health, is failing to address the hugely significant role that our emotions and our mental and spiritual well-being play in having a healthy heart and how we can take responsibility for addressing these for ourselves. I read the book in one sitting I was so gripped by what it had to say. If your heart has literally been aching then it's time to wonder what you are doing in life, and why. The Lunatic Gene will hold those questions up to you from start to finish. By the end your heart will already have started to answer them."

Alan Sharland. Director at CAOS Conflict Management

"In today's world that is so full of dis-ease, unhappiness and suffering, Adam Shaw shines forth with his wisdom and experience to share with you some of the most important factors for keeping your heart healthy and living a life free from guilt, regret and to having a life of meaning. His wit, stories and passion come through in this light- hearted but poignant book on learning how NOT to be on your death bed with regrets and illness. He provides ways and advice on how to live a life of joy, humour and connectedness. As Adam demonstrates - If you love YOU and that amazing heart of yours, the world will follow!"

Amanda Steadman. Author of Connect To Authentic Success

"For most of us, with our ever-accelerating, tightly optimised western life-styles, any physical or emotional signals from our bodies are quickly dismissed as unwanted impediments to ticking off our stuffed to-do-lists. Apparently, as long as we 'function', all is well. Undoubtedly, denial is a powerful thing! This madness only comes to a - temporary - halt, when we, close friends or family members suddenly break down with a heart attack, stroke or burnout.

Adam Shaw, acclaimed holistic health expert, author and public speaker, explains the reason behind this madness - and gives us tools to help us to solve it BEFORE disaster strikes. Set on his own journey through years of working in critical care with severely ill and dying patients, he has successfully condensed his insight and experience into practical tips to finally understand why we're doing what we're doing – and how to set ourselves on a better, healthier path by listening to the innate intelligence of our heart – in the proverbial AND literal sense. Rather than fighting our destructive impulses, which Adam terms The Lunatic Gene, he teaches us to dance with them.

Knowing Adam personally, I knew this book would make for an entertaining read, as it is written in the same chatty and humorous tone that earned him acclaim as a public speaker. I found the content frightfully on target in regards to my own life situation. Furthermore, It provided a much-needed fresh perspective on why things are the way they are and how to change them. Get ready to rock and roll, I say!"

Chris Sauerwein

"Adam Shaw's thought provoking book The Lunatic Gene is written in an entertaining style while at the same time as giving a serious message about ensuring one's heart is kept healthy. More a recipe for living a happy and healthy life, I believe this book should be required reading for everyone – not just those recovering from heart attacks and heart disease!"

Pam Lawrence, Coach & Stress Management Therapist

"Witty, sharp, poignant and honest, this book is a gem. Adam has written a unique view on life and manages to appeal to all!"

Rosanne Shochot, Recruitment Specialist at David Alan Consultants

"Adam shares his moving journey and adds heart to it. Must read for anyone wanting to know how to deal with life, when things don't always seem to go to plan or when you sabotage it yourself. Find out the strategies you can use to turn things around and make The Lunatic Gene your friend. When the mind rules the heart it's a recipe for disaster, so love a little bit more!"

Bobby Gill

Welcome to The Lunatic Gene

In reading this, you will get to know your Lunatic Gene through understanding how self-love, happiness, and unlocking the barriers to these, are the keys to understanding every other relationship in your life, regardless how challenging or amazing they are. You will discover how your head and heart communicate, and the role of your Lunatic Gene in distorting this information. Unless all three are aligned, your health will suffer and you will not be enjoying your life. If you want to feel better more often, this book is your gentle inroad, supplemented with practical steps, to show you exactly how.

If you are reading this, the odds are that you already identify with The Lunatic Gene. We all have it. It is usually more evident within your family relationships. You probably have a few issues with one or two of your nearest and dearest! This book will help you to navigate your family dynamics more harmoniously.

Your Lunatic Gene is often the part of you that reacts to pressure, stress or criticism, and it can cause two extreme reactions. The first will drive you to habits that you know aren't strictly good for you, but you do them anyway. Drinking too much alcohol, smoking, and poor dietary choices that can cause weight issues are just some of the not so positive manifestations of your Lunatic Gene. Please note the words *too much* in the previous sentence. Exactly what too much is will be down to your thoughts and feelings on the subject. All habits in moderation can be balanced and are not an issue unless you think they are. This will be discussed later in the book.

In it's other extreme, The Lunatic Gene turns negativity into drive and motivation. When this happens you get people who change the world in very positive ways.

Your Life's Lunatic Adventure

In your life right now you are on a journey of discovery. That adventure is whatever you make it. You will never know when life is going to end for you, or the people who mean the most to you. However, many people never consider this until it's too late. Reading The Lunatic Gene is your insurance policy for you managing this unpredictable certainty in your life a little better.

In its most positive light, people are inspired to do incredible things, with amazing results. Think Gandhi, Nelson Mandela, and Mother Teresa. Most people would have thought that they were lunatics for even attempting to do what they did at the beginning of their journeys. Have you ever had an idea that other people have shot down in flames? How did this affect you? Your response will be how your Lunatic Gene is currently showing up in your life.

What You Can Expect

This book is not the answer to the meaning of your life. It is simply a guide and a few questions that will show you how lunacy plays out in your world, and how to channel that into the best adventure you've ever had. This type of lunacy is not just the element that can guide you to unhealthy thoughts and habits, it is also the element of you that can make you live an exceptional life, and change the world in a positive way. Because most people will never even consider this, you may well be considered a lunatic for thinking big, being unique, and doing things differently to the masses.

This book will show you who you really are and how you are living in a crazy world. Your family are testament to that. If for any reason they are not: congratulations! You are either very lucky, or have clearly reached a state of inner harmony that allows you to love your life, despite any doubt from anyone around you. You clearly already have a strong sense of purpose and certainty within you.

If this is not you, I invite you to read on. This book will help you to feel happier. If you do not love yourself totally, it is because of your Lunatic Gene. This book is an explanation of why this happens, and what you can do to make your life better. Ultimately, it is an exploration of your relationship with yourself. Working on this makes it is far easier to increase your wellbeing, resilience and relationships.

This book is a light-hearted guide to the early warning symptoms of serious illness, and what you can do about it. Not everyone who reads it will make sense of their life. Indeed, this is as much a guide as to why life often doesn't seem to make sense, as it is to how it can.

Whatever reason you choose for wanting to know more about your Lunatic Gene, which is a part of who you are, I welcome you to this journey.

Adam Shaw - The Heart Guy

About This Book

Back in 1992 I started my nurse training. Had I read this book then I wouldn't have believed a lot of the things I now write about. It took many years of searching, self-development and seeking help to reach any sort of sense on many of the things in this book. On that basis I tell you not to believe me in what I have to say. I simply suggest that you take what resonates with you and drop anything that doesn't. As your life and experience progress you may find your mind opening to certain concepts that you read here that seemed ridiculous when you first read them.

This book is a bit like watching a film as a child, then re-visiting it as an adult – the key message will be different on each occasion (I will use Star Wars as a good analogy from personal experience). There will be something of value for everyone, but only if you take action towards it. I can guarantee that if you re-read this book in a year or so you will have very different take-outs of the content.

The difference between knowledge and wisdom is action. Be careful what you know, because knowing something, and actually living it is the difference between lunacy and happiness.

About You

Whatever made you start reading this is largely immaterial. The fact is: You are now here. You have a part of you that causes you to do lunatic things, and probably perceive that you have a lunatic or two in your family. How these things manifest can either make your life great, or make you ill. This book will explain how your relationship with yourself decides this, and the factors influencing your decision.

The information in this book is to your sanity what showering is to your cleanliness. If you use it regularly your life will improve: If not, it will not. There is no point complaining that showering doesn't work, when you don't use one for a few months. The techniques and suggestions in this book work on exactly the same principle.

Some of what I will share with you may make sense, some may not: decide for yourself, and enjoy the journey. Most importantly of all: however seemingly crazy your family or life seem right now, there are many others who feel the same. All of this is designed to draw certain people together to make sense of their situation, grow in confidence, and live happier, more fulfilling lives. As an individual you can make a difference, but only when you are surrounded by the right team. If you are ready to discover a better you and a better team, this book will help you.

Table of Contents

Introduction

I watched from a distance as a man in a suit walked into the middle of the fire

The Lunatic Gene (n) The genealogical cause of thought processes that lead to either illness and early death, or success beyond what most people would deem possible.

You will not find *The Lunatic Gene* in any science or biology books. It is the innocuous assassin, or the revolutionary leader running amok in your DNA, causing you to react to stress, guilt, judgement, and unhappiness in your life. It is also the crusader who trail blazes paths where others fear to tread. This book explains this phenomenon and offers you some help in understanding how your *Lunatic Gene* works and how to harness it in a more positive way.

You will never make sense of life through the lens of reason. You are an emotional being, and act accordingly. Whenever you are in a highly emotional state your capacity to act logically is massively reduced. Therefore, to justify life through logic is madness. This will be explained in much more detail in chapter 5. It is not the absence of information and knowledge that causes unhappiness, suffering and disease: it is the lack of application. *The Lunatic Gene* is the cause of this.

Most things you want to achieve in your life, you probably already know what you have to do to get them. You just, for some reason, don't do it. The same can be said of most major lifestyle choices. This book will not change your life, it's simply another portal of information. It will, however, explain how your heart functions from a psychological perspective. It will also demonstrate how *The Lunatic Gene* either causes greatness, or stops many people from ever being happy and fulfilled, highlighting its activity as a primary contributor towards illness, disease and premature death. For some people this

1

manifests as low-level unhappiness. For others this leads to acts of true madness. I have witnessed several of these in my life.

Where this journey began

When I was ten years old, my dad took me to the fireworks night at the psychiatric hospital where we lived and grew up. Both of my parents worked there as nurses and we lived in the staff accommodation within the hospital grounds. My sister and I stood holding dad's hand, watching the bonfire and fireworks provided by the hospital. With patients, staff and their families watching, the fire rose to over six metres in height. The heat from the fire on this cold night was intense, even from where we stood, at least ten metres back. I had witnessed many strange things as a child growing up in a psychiatric hospital. However, I had not expected what was about to unfold.

I watched from a distance as a man in a suit walked into the middle of the fire

I saw his face as he walked in, which had an intensity and focus I had not seen before, or since this incident. The flames consumed him swiftly. I had known that it was tradition to burn a guy on Guy Fawkes Night, but I was surprised to see that they were using a real guy this year! Eventually, a handful of nurses did manage to remove him from the fire, and an ambulance soon arrived to try and help him. At this stage I realised that this had not been part of the original plan. It took the man three days to die.

I wondered what could cause someone to do this

Over thirty years later, after working with thousands of people with health issues, and studying human behaviour, energy medicine, alternative therapies, personal development, regression, hypnotherapy, Neuro-Linguistic Programming and an array of other health and healing systems, I have gained some insight into what may have happened that day. Allied with over thirteen years' working as a nurse on three different continents, with people who were seriously ill, I have learnt there are certain recurrent patterns which are early warning symptoms of dis-ease.

Whilst these may not be as extreme as to land you in an asylum or bonfire, if you are unhappy with any of your relationships, your job, yourself or your life, your heart is already in a state of dis-ease. This is probably the reason you found this book and started to read it. If left untreated, this can lead to your own heart attacking you, or another serious illness developing. Since more people die from their own heart attacking them than anything else on the planet right now, it may be a good idea to discover the agenda of *The Lunatic Gene* and prevent an attack before it's too late.

The bottom line

I have gained an understanding of what becomes important to people as they are about to die, how the heart works and the nature of *The Lunatic Gene*. This is the reason that you know how you could improve your life, but inevitably don't. This hidden aspect of your nature - which most medical experts fail to mention - is the same phenomenon that explains why unhealthy habits, sickness and absenteeism amongst medical staff are far more prevalent than in the corporate world.

If you love yourself and wake up feeling good every day, facing life fearlessly and turning challenges into triumphs, you absolutely do not need to read this book. Your Lunatic Gene is operating positively, turning criticism and setbacks into determination and driven action towards your goals. If this is you this book will bring you little benefit. Unless, of course, you derive pleasure from hearing about the random insights and reflections of a chap you have probably never heard of before.

If, however, you are living in fear, depression, apathy, pain and/or have depressive thoughts, this book may provide you with some insight as to why. My musings may even bring a smile to your face. At the very least it will give you the knowledge that there are many others out there feeling the same way as you. This is a journey that will explain how the wellbeing of your heart is affected by your head and thoughts, which are constantly affected by *The Lunatic Gene*. It can also help you feel better, have more energy, be happier, and improve your relationships with yourself, others and life.

Death is certain. Life is optional

I am not an expert or a model of perfect health. I enjoy occasional indulgences that would definitely not be considered strictly healthy by purists in the field. I am also prone to occasional risky adventures, cunning plans and random outbursts of ridiculousness. I have faced death, worked with the dying and their families and swum with crocodiles - albeit unintentionally. I believe judgement and guilt are the biggest killers in the world, all manifested through *The Lunatic Gene*. This book is the result of my own journey towards some sort of self-acceptance of over forty years of relative insanity. I used to fight *The Lunatic Gene*: now I accept and dance with it.

If you are ready to discover a way to be a little bit happier, accepting your quirks and lunatic tendencies, this book can be your sat-nav to a better life through freeing yourself from the judgement of others, releasing guilt and showing you another way. I believe that everyone has lunatic tendencies, regardless how slight and/or innocuous. This book is an exploration of that trait. Although I use the word 'lunatic' frequently in this book, this is me making light of a very serious subject. On this premise, I make one clear distinction: anyone who would harm themselves, or anyone else, does not qualify for my call to action below. I advise you seek professional advice. There are also plenty of resources on my website www.adamshaw.co

"Lunatics of the world unite. You have nothing to lose but your neuroses."

Love,

Adam Shaw. The Heart Guy x

P.S.

Did you know that this book is associated with a video course?

www.thelunaticgene.com/course

Chapter 1. Life's Only Guarantee

Death: You never know when you will face it

Screams were piercing my ears from everyone else around me. I was lying on a chap, who was shouting out in pain. He was trapped under the huge, 1 tonne plus, 4x4 Unimog in which we had been travelling. His legs were pinned between the vehicle and the mountain growth. Our bemused driver stumbled around in a daze as petrol poured out from above him in the now upside-down vehicle. Meanwhile, the girl next to me could hardly breathe fast enough to emit the continuous high-pitched screams as she surveyed the carnage, with a small drop of blood trickling down her leg from the scratch she had sustained.

Bodies were piled in different places, in various states of lucidity, and some injuries had been sustained. This was like a scene from a horror film, except this time I was in it. However, somehow I had escaped with not a single injury and found myself feeling serene. I realised I had to take control of the situation. My career as a nurse had prepared me well for such crisis situations, and I knew I had to act immediately.

I swiftly realised the chap who had broken my fall, to his own detriment, would very shortly lose the circulation in his legs if the pressure were not quickly relieved. My assessment of the situation indicated his was the most pressing of all - quite literally. I stood on the undergrowth below him, which was clamping his legs under the Unimog, and pulled on the side of the vehicle to reduce the vice-like grip trapping his legs. This gave him just a little more room for his blood to circulate. From here, I began to reassure him we would get him out soon.

Our South African off-road trip had certainly delivered

I had been on a trip along the South African Wild Coast back in 2001, on an off-road tour, when a ridiculous piece of parking by the locals had caused us to roll down a mountain. Fortunately, we did not roll far, as a large thicket had broken our fall. There were no seat belts in our 4x4 for the twelve or so passengers. As I bounced around during the fall, time appeared to slow down, and I knew there was nothing I could do to control the situation. In spite of this, I felt completely relaxed.

On a narrow mountain road, two locals had decided to stop their cars and talk to each other, leaning out of their car windows on opposite sides of the road. As we came around the corner, we had realised there was only room for one car to fit through the gap they had left, and there was a car coming the other way. Our driver had little choice but to swerve off the path and down the mountainside. It was either this or take a full-on collision with one of the other cars.

As blood and carnage surrounded me, I was able to stay calm and prevent the chap below me from losing his legs

Our curiously parked companions jumped on top of the vehicle to see what damage they had caused, increasing the weight on the trapped guy's legs. I suggested to them this might not have been the best of ideas! Meanwhile, our tour leader came out of his daze and screamed at them to get a jack. They did, and it was placed under the vehicle, allowing the release of my new friend's trapped legs. I knew at this point I was very lucky, not just to be alive, but also to have walked away after rolling off a mountain road without getting a scratch on me - and not having been wearing a seatbelt, due to none being available.

Having rolled my car at age seventeen, finishing upside-down, suspended by my seatbelt, in the woods, (once again, without a scratch on me) I was starting to feel very lucky indeed.

These incidents allowed me to start looking at the world differently and to be open to new insights and experiences. Retrospectively, I knew if I had died, there would be much in my life I would have changed if I'd known I was about to die. Things I should have said and done kept popping up into my awareness. What would I regret the most? What was truly important in life? My life would never be the same after coming so close to death for the second time, in the South African mountains.

Life only offers you one guarantee

One day you will be dead. In the time that elapses, whether it is months, days, minutes or seconds between you realising you are dying, and actual death, your big regrets will flash through your mind and one question you will almost definitely have is "Did I ever really live?" If that moment should happen today, and you do not feel you have really lived, you already have some stage of dis-ease.   I use dis-ease deliberately, rather than disease. I have learnt that when you are not experiencing flow, love and/or happiness in your life, this state of dis-ease can be the early warning indicator of heart disease, manifested through your mind via The Lunatic Gene.

The good news is, if you live long enough to finish reading this book, you have a wonderful opportunity to not only reverse your symptoms, but also to live a slightly happier, healthier and more meaningful life.

What is The Lunatic Gene?

Before you go running to Google to find out about this phenomenon, let me save you the task. To my knowledge, this gene has never been studied - or even identified. It is simply a phenomenon based on the behaviours I have witnessed in global affairs, within myself and of clients I have nursed through illness, and when facing death.

It is the trait that stops you from living a life of fearless adventure. It is the aspect of your being which stops you from following your heart, as your head talks you out of it, or can drive you to follow your heart when everyone else is telling you something cannot or shouldn't be done. The Lunatic Gene is my terminology for the paradoxes of human nature that can lead to fear, depression, unhappiness, pain, disease and early death. Guilt, judgement and false beliefs are its causes, whilst self-acceptance, trust and love are the prescription to training your Lunatic Gene to counter such symptoms, through modifying your beliefs and behaviours accordingly.

If you believed everything written about potential risk factors for a heart attack, it is likely you would be too paranoid to eat anything or go anywhere

I have seen so many people disempowered by the belief that everything their doctor tells them is absolute. What if doctors were not always in possession of all of the facts? I have read referral letters from General Practitioners to hospital doctors, and can confirm many do not have a clue about certain aspects of health and disease.

In fairness to doctors, they only get a few minutes with which to help each patient. It is just not possible to get to the root of a problem in such a short time for most people. Consequently, drugs are prescribed which can relieve the current symptoms, although often they cause other issues. Drugs are not likely, however, to combat the real cause of your symptoms. This is down to your beliefs, actions and ability to discover what your heart wants you to know. We will look at this in more detail later on.

Because of the nature of many drugs given in the treatment of heart disease, there are sometimes related side effects. This can often turn the treatment of your heart into a lottery.

A new way of thinking

Fortunately, more and more people are tuning into the intelligence of their heart, and realising it is separate to the intelligence of their head. Only through aligning the two can you have a truly healthy heart and body. This process involves the acknowledgement of The Lunatic Gene and how it can distort logic.

What if it were possible to predict your chances of having a heart attack and other diseases such as strokes and cancer, years before they happened? Is it possible your choices have the power to control whether you have a serious disease or not?

Having spent over thirteen years working as a nurse, and talking to many people who have experienced heart attacks, there is a common theme with all of them - they didn't see it coming. Disillusionment and surprise are often common in sufferers. This is often because many people who have had a heart attack had become an expert in ignoring the symptoms.

Your awareness of the progression of heart disease can often be tracked back to the point when you first stopped truly loving yourself, or things just didn't seem to make sense. If you knew this, and did nothing about it, you already have a symptom of heart dis-ease. Frequently, the origin is far deeper rooted.

There is no way of ignoring the statistics. Heart attacks kill more people than anything else on this planet right now. Since your heart is central to your life, circulating your life-blood, it makes sense to understand it from physiological, mental, emotional and spiritual points of view. Unfortunately, my initial experience of the medical establishment indicated practitioners tended to focus mainly on the physical symptoms, often neglecting many of the mental, emotional and spiritual aspects of heart wellbeing. This is tantamount to checking only one tyre on your car and deciding the other three must be in perfect, working shape as a result.

Not understanding the message of your heart for a prolonged period can lead to a heart attack

Fortunately, there are usually decades of symptoms before a heart attack happens, but if you have had chest pain, palpitations or a heart attack, then it's time to listen: or serious consequences will result. There is no way of softening this blow. I've watched people die very young who had not understood their heart had a message for them, as their Lunatic Gene justified all sorts of slowly suicidal practices.

Start by asking: have you ever had a *feeling* something is missing in your life but you didn't know what? If so, this is your heart's call to action. It wants you to *feel* its message. It wants you to listen to its call. It wants you to be happier, healthier and wealthier. To do this, your heart realises it may need to send you increasingly bigger and more serious wake-up symptoms to jolt your head into action.

Your head is for thinking. Your heart is for feeling

If you are lost in thought about what caused your heart attack, chest pain or palpitations, then this is very common. Heart attacks can happen when you do not listen to, or act upon, your feelings. Your thoughts generate chemicals in your brain, causing your heart to feel emotion. When you are not happy with how you feel, your heart wants you to change your thinking. If you do not, you are open to heart disease. When your emotion becomes the most important guide in your life, you are on the right track to discovering your heart's true message.

If you are ready to listen to your heart, you can discover what it wants you to know

Your heart is in constant communication with your head, generating 40-60 times the electrical amplitude of your brain. Your heart developed before your brain when you were a foetus. Your heart beats independently of your brain and has its own complex nervous system, also known as the heart brain, which is constantly communicating with your head.

Your heart signals especially affect the brain centres involved in decision-making, creativity and emotional experience. Your heart is central to all positive experiences you have. When you learn how to align your head and your heart, it will instantly enhance your mood, motivation, relationships and health.

A little extra effort now can save a massive amount of pain later

Like planning for your retirement, it is not a good idea to wait until you are 65 to find out whether you have enough money to retire on. Most people appreciate the need to educate themselves about pensions, investments and retirement well before they retire, when it is important to make small and regular investments over an extended period. When working with the health of your heart, it is exactly the same principle.

However, I have found for most people who have had heart attacks or have serious illnesses, they make no investments in their health until it is too late. In my experience, very few people like to admit all is not well in their lives, and become adept at ignoring the symptoms. I include myself for many years in this equation. The Lunatic Gene can do funny things to one's psyche! Unfortunately, heart health is much more than simply the absence of disease.

Just by being open-minded as you read this book, learning how to tune into your heart and recognising when The Lunatic Gene is playing with your head, you can dramatically increase your chances of leading a longer, healthier, happier life. By doing this yourself, you are far more likely to be able to help those whom you love to do the same.

The day I changed my mind

As a nurse, I watched people die, and witnessed the aftermath of tragic news being broken to various families. Between this, and watching people being stripped of hope as they found out their illnesses were terminal, I started looking for answers. My openness to new ideas, and other systems of health, was accelerated when my grandfather was diagnosed with terminal cancer.

If you have ever been in a situation where a loved one knew they were going to die, then you will know the pain of knowing you were not able to help them.

I had heard of a thing called Reiki. I knew little about what it was, but had been told it enabled healing to occur, and anyone could do it.

I wasn't the only person in my family to have little idea of what Reiki was

When I told my dad I had paid a substantial amount of money to do a weekend of Reiki, he nearly choked on his drink. Moments later he informed me that, if I wanted to learn raking, then he would teach me for £10 in the back garden!

Reiki pointed me in the right direction

After attending a Reiki course and working on myself for 6 weeks, I developed an ache in my chest, which worsened each time I performed Reiki on it. Ironically, I was working on a Cardiac Care Unit at the time, and had to cancel my shifts because of the pain. I knew it wasn't angina, but had no idea what it was.

One day I was in so much pain during a healing, it led to a breakthrough. I realised that although my body was in great physical shape, my mind-set was catapulting me towards heart disease. I was not able to save the life of my grandfather, but I was able to better help him at the end of his life. I was also grateful for saving my own life. Despite being in great shape physically, I had been more dead than alive in my mind-set.

I thought about my life and what it would have meant to me if I'd died

I could not remember the last time I had told a family member I loved them. We did not use the word 'love' much in our family. I had made career choices to please them, and not myself, ended up in relationships where I was afraid of expressing how I really felt, and was taking regular recreational drugs to numb the feeling that something was missing in my life. This epiphany made me realise I had been operating through The Lunatic Gene, and needed to make changes in my life - quickly.

I was like Scrooge on Christmas morning

I went to all of my family and close friends to tell them how much I loved them. Admittedly, this was a little awkward after a lifetime of repression and spectacular failure to be honest emotionally. Many of my family and friends started asking me what drugs I had been taking to cause these uncharacteristic outbursts. Fortunately, I was soon able to relieve them of this notion and have a profound sharing experience with all of them. Each interaction caused the pain in my chest to lessen. When I had done this with all of my family and closest friends, I felt pain-free and fantastic.

I had never told my grandfather how much I loved him before this. He was a tough guy and it had never seemed appropriate. By sharing loving thoughts with him as he was dying with cancer, I was able to create a meaningful moment, which will stay with me for the rest of my life. I knew then I could not save everyone: that sometimes healing involves letting go and helping people to die a little more peacefully.

The biggest problem I had was that 'I had never realised that I had a problem'

Because I was surrounded by madness, disease and death in my job, I had always considered myself pretty fit and healthy. I worked as a part-time fitness instructor and exercised 4-6 times every week. I could not have possibly comprehended how I could be a candidate for heart disease, yet I was. Since that day, I have been making small investments in my future health by looking after myself a little better and being a little more honest with myself and those I spend time with.

This is not to say I live a perfectly healthy lifestyle: I do not. However, compared to where I was ten years ago, I am in better shape mentally, emotionally and spiritually, if not quite physically! Like a pension, small investments now can have a huge impact later. You can add years of quality living to your life if you are willing to invest your time in reading this book, and to making some small changes.

Chapter 2. Life's Lunatic Asylum

Did you ever have a feeling you didn't belong somewhere? Maybe this happened at school, in a group, in a job or at a party? Usually, when this happens, you get to question how it was possible you ever ended up in this position. Is it possible you have compromised your own life in order to help others, or protect the feelings of someone else?

From the asylum to insanity and beyond!

Growing up in a psychiatric hospital was an interesting experience. I realise this may not be the most acceptable description, but back in the 1970s, political correctness had not quite made it to the grounds of sunny Hertfordshire. Geriatric patients in their pyjamas and slippers, some with no teeth or dentures, looking for cigarettes had, however, made it to our doorstep frequently. Some of them would mistake the front lawns in our avenue for public toilets! This was a normal part of my life as I grew up.

At school I was known as a *nutter* by some of the children in my class. This reputation proved to be most useful in staying out of the way of those whom I considered to be the real nutters, of which there were a few in my school. It was not exactly renowned for its great academic record and development of upstanding members of the community.

I watched psychiatric patients spend most of their days sitting on park benches surrounded by nature. Consequently, I spent a lot of my youth immersed in nature and having fun exploring the grounds of the hospital and the surrounding areas.

The real insanity

It wasn't until I left the lunatic asylum that I realised what real lunacy was. At the age of seventeen I joined a Japanese bank, working with several people who had been there for decades. Whilst some of them appeared to be relatively happy, most were counting their years to retirement, complaining about their job and were generally very pessimistic about their lives.

Meanwhile, there is killing all over the world, mass suffering, suicide, misery and poverty. Many of those who are not killing, starving or physically compromised, spend their time working in jobs they don't like, to pay for things they don't really need, to try to impress people they don't even care for. The saddest thing is, that when I asked my patients who had just had heart attacks what they really wanted in life – they often didn't know. Would you go on holiday without knowing where you were going? Most people would not, yet in life this is how most people go about it. It's like packing, going to the airport, and hoping you will be able to go where you will have the best holiday experience.

Do you know exactly what you want?

In life, the difference between knowledge and wisdom is action. If you feel driven to take some positive action, write a journal and document how you feel now, and write some goals you have which would improve your life. Whilst you may be tempted to read on without taking this into account, I will go on to explain how this could be of benefit if you ever decide to help yourself more. The action of taking time to consider exactly how you feel, and allowing the writing to take you to where it needs to, can be a very powerful exercise.

I realise many people have become so trained in ignoring how they feel; this exercise may take a bit more work. If getting in touch with your feelings does not come naturally, then start off by writing, "I'm not exactly sure how I feel but the first thing that comes into my head is…"

Writing things down may not be your thing. In this case you can record your thoughts on audio or video. Audio and video journals work well. The best part about them is you get a very real picture of where you are at this point of your journey, and exactly how far you have come when you review it down the line.

Why should you bother with any sort of writing?

If you have ever had the same thought(s) about the same issue(s), then you know already how easy it is to get caught up in cycles that do not help you feel better. When these thoughts circle in your head, like a scratched record, then it can take a toll on your general health, well-being and life.

It is perfectly human to get stuck in thoughts occasionally. When you find yourself feeling stuck or lost, and don't know who to talk to about it - or even if you want to talk to anyone about it - writing can be an invaluable tool.

If you have never kept a journal, then it will be difficult to fully explain to you the benefits of writing down what you think, feel or want.

When you don't know what you want, you will get more of what you don't want. This is why it is important to know what you want in order to attract it into your life.

The law of attrACTION

I realise the Law of Attraction has been popular in recent years. There are some who are amazed at what they can attract into their lives, and others left despondent by their lack of results. This is because action is necessary in order for attraction to occur. If things are not working for you, then you must take action if you want things to change. Sitting on your couch, feeling sorry for yourself and waiting for the universe to deliver you mountains of abundance is just not realistic. If you are not *feeling* good then do something to change it.

When you do something different, there will be no shortage of people wanting to pull you back

Be different: realise the people who made the biggest impact in the world all had to face adversity, and had to do something different to that which everyone else was telling them at some point.

Nelson Mandela had to spend 27 years in jail to stay true to the message in his heart. Martin Luther King and Gandhi were killed, as they suspected they would be, because they voiced the message of their hearts. Richard Branson is a multi-millionaire, who is having a positive influence worldwide, because he followed his heart, even when there were plenty of people telling him it couldn't be done.

What does your heart want you to know?

If you are feeling apathy, uncertainty, fear, frustration, anger, trapped or overwhelmed, then your heart is using its power to inform your head something needs to change before it resorts to an attack. Its message is not always clear, and there may be a leap of faith involved, as The Lunatic Gene has a powerful influence in distorting this message. However, is it not better to shoot for the stars and not get there, than to hold back in fear, and wonder whether you could have done it at the end of your life?

Some bridges need to be burned

In 2007 I finally left my nursing job because my heart was calling towards a greater goal. I would let my nurse registration expire to make it more difficult for me to ever go back. I never have. I had known nursing was not my place for years before I left it.

My heart has been calling me to take a new path, to write this book and to do what I can to help make sense of my life and the paradoxical nuttiness of dancing with The Lunatic Gene.

With that in mind, let us now look at what else you will learn if you choose to read on...

Chapter 3. What You Will Learn

First, we will look at the relationship between your head and heart. How they work, what drives them and how it is easy to become out of alignment. When this happens, heart dis-ease begins. You will get to understand and feel the symptoms moment-to-moment, by understanding how your Emotional Guidance System (EGS) works. Knowing this, alone, will stand you in better stead when it comes to knowing where you are, and whether you are safe or not. It will also give you a template for knowing whether you, your friends and family are being influenced by The Lunatic Gene, or not.

You will also get to question your family dynamics and whether they are currently working for you, your relationships with others and your relationship with yourself. You will also be given potentially powerful insights to plant seeds of awareness, which may not bring you instant results right now. They may, however, lay the foundations for a breakthrough down the line, in time to prevent a heart attack or serious, premature illness.

You will discover why some people are resistant to healing, how to use your language to get better results in your life, and to make sense of even your most challenging situations. You will know how to change your mood instantly. At the end of the book you will be invited to take the journey further, thus giving you practical steps and support to help you on your quest to live with your Lunatic Gene in a more harmonious way.

You will also discover the healing power of thought and how it can change your life. Find out how simply focusing on what positive outcome you would like in your life, right now, can dramatically increase the chance of it happening. This is a journey of discovery.

Relax and be light-hearted as often as you can

I am a big fan of comedy, especially Monty Python. The films: 'The Life of Brian' and 'The Quest for the Holy Grail' were pivotal to me during my youth. My dad let me watch 'The Quest for the Holy Grail' when I was just five years old. He had to stop the film twice, because I couldn't breathe properly through the laughter.

Maintaining a sense of humour is possibly the most powerful healing tool you have

If there are any funny videos or stories that make you laugh, then watch or read them regularly. If you have any friends who usually tend to make you laugh, then they will be like gold dust to you throughout this process. Call them regularly and give them permission to laugh at your heaviest, most challenging issues. There is something about laughter that can transform even the darkest situations.

You will need all of these light-hearted resources when you start to look at the early warning symptoms of disease in the next chapter, which most doctors do not even think to warn you about.

Chapter 4. The Early Warning Symptoms of Disease

Early warning symptoms of disease usually start decades before a serious illness occurs. I realise this is not something commonly acknowledged in current medical circles, unless you subscribe to the genetic theory of predisposition to certain diseases being just part of life's family lottery. The Lunatic Gene is a subtle beast at times.

I am not here to discredit the belief that if your parents had a disease, you are more likely to get it. There is plenty of evidence to suggest this is the case. I am going to suggest to you this school of thought is more than just a little disempowering in its current form, and there may be another possibility.

Make up your own mind

Is it true you have genes that predispose you towards certain illnesses? And is there nothing you can do to change it? Even if this were true, it would not be very helpful to you if your family had a history of disease or illness. I have found everyone I worked with who believed this theory had resigned their fate to the lap of the gods. Consequently, less than healthy habits were more likely to ensue, worry and disempowerment prevailed, as people believed their fate was out of their hands anyway.

The thought that there was a genetic cause for illness made many feel there was little they could do to stop it. I have spoken to people who lived in fear of disease for several years, prior to getting it. Reaching the age where a parent had their serious illness/early death is often a particularly stressful experience.

What if it were possible that the only reason people are more likely to have a heart attack, if it runs in their family, was because they learnt many of the same habits and beliefs as their parents? If you grow up in a household where your parents smoke, it stands to reason you are more likely to smoke when you get older. If your parents believe they are likely to get a heart attack because their parent(s) did, it is much more likely you will believe the same thing. We are all influenced by our parents' beliefs.

Handing you back control

Ultimately, either could be true, both are plausible, but one is a disempowering belief, handing control of your future away from you. The other is an empowering belief, increasing the chances of you taking control of your health and future - also giving you hope. My experience in this field has indicated this evidence to be irrefutable. Those who believe they have control of their health and future have a much better chance of getting better and making better lifestyle choices. Some call this the placebo effect.

If you knew you had the power to prevent premature, serious illness, would you not be prepared to take your health and wellbeing just a little more seriously? I have seen people who have heart attacks, or who were diagnosed with cancer, give up lifetime habits, instantly. Often, they had previously believed this would not be possible.

It is not whether you can do something; this is for certain. It's only a question of whether you have enough motivation

Most of my patients during my nursing days would just laugh at me, or ignore any warnings about regular smoking, lack of exercise or poor diet leading to an early death. Until faced with the real situation of knowing your days are few, it is unlikely you will be able to access the same motivation it can bring.

Motivation is often brought about by a loved one

I have known more people who gave up smoking because their partner or children didn't like the smell of their breath, than those who gave up because they thought it might kill them one day! Having a good friend or close family member diagnosed with a terminal disease can also have an effect on the health habits of a friend or family member. Unfortunately, for many families, they do not express how they really feel about their family members, until death is close. Even then, it provides a significant challenge to most.

This is especially apparent amongst people who have had a para-suicide attempt (someone who doesn't really want to kill themselves, but damages them self as a cry for help). Unfortunately, some people who do this don't realise some of the potential complications they could experience – and they die anyway. This is particularly common with drug overdoses. Paracetamol was the most common offender during my time as a nurse. It can be particularly nasty when overdosed on, often taking the person several days to die as they break down from within. Almost always, this three-day period is enough for them to change their minds about wanting to die.

Let us now look at the symptoms of heart disease

Rather than start at the earliest warning signs, I will take you the other way. Since all of my patients usually had to experience angina or a heart attack to be receptive to this, I will take you through the journey I would take the patients through, and the questions I would ask them.

Prior to your heart attack, did you ever get episodes of short, stabbing pains in your chest, sometimes lasting just a fraction of a second (angina), or feel your heart was pounding against your chest (palpitations)?

The answer to this question was usually 'yes'. In my experience, one or both of these two symptoms often (though not always) come before a heart attack. This is the 'last chance saloon' on the symptomatic journey to a heart attack. Also known as angina, this state is caused by the lack of blood to the heart and a lack of understanding of the early warning symptoms. Angina can last for just a fraction of a second. It appears like a needle stabbing inside your chest.

Prior to this, there are usually other medical warning indicators which doctors do alert you to: diabetes, hypertension and obesity. All are warning symptoms for a heart attack, but the root of these is deeper. The question I always asked someone who was admitted with a heart attack or angina pains was the same.

What has been causing you more stress than normal over the past 6 months – 1 year?

I have yet to find someone admitted with a heart attack or serious illness that could not answer this straight away. The stress response of your body is great if you are in a situation where you need to be prepared for fight or flight. It greatly restricts the flow of blood to all non-essential organs, fills your body with stimulants and prepares you for strenuous, physical activity.

This is great if you have just run into a lion in the jungle, but not so great if you spend most of your day in an office. This surge of adrenaline can lead to multiple imbalances in the body. This can result in regular tiredness, loss of appetite, irritability, reduced concentration and performance, and extreme mood swings. This can affect sleep patterns and cause chaos with your routines. Because regular stress in an environment where people are not active has no way to release, the residual effects become increasingly hazardous. Stress can be both useful, and dangerous if not addressed.

Are you currently happy in your job and personal relationships?

These are the two areas I find consistently out of place for those who have heart attacks. Usual excuses for those who endure long-term, personal relationships which lack harmony are, "We only stay together for the kids", "Where else would I go?" "I couldn't possibly afford to leave", and "It could be worse…"

For those who get stuck in jobs which they end up hating, common excuses are, "I couldn't possibly afford to leave", "I would never earn nearly as much money anywhere else", "We have become used to the money", "So many people have been laid off - I'm lucky to still have a job" and "I don't have the skills to do anything else".

Being unhappy in a job or relationship can have people in an almost continuous state of fight or flight as they wrestle with the mental prison they have constructed for themselves. Fear of the alternatives and the unknown are the main motivators for maintaining this status quo. Add a challenging boss to the equation, who never gets confronted, and you have a recipe for heart disaster. Sleeplessness and mood swings are very common side effects in this state.

Have you had, or are you having, a mid-life crisis?

Everyone has their own interpretation of what a mid-life crisis is. For this reason I am not going to look at the standard definitions. I offer you the following indicators. This is by no means a comprehensive guide. I encourage you to add or delete anything to find out what it has meant, or would mean, to you.

Symptoms of a mid-life crisis can include:

- **The feeling** something is missing from your life, but you don't know what it is

- **The longing** for more excitement or adventure

- **Knowing** you may have wasted some of the healthiest and/or best days of your life doing things you didn't love

- **Wondering** how you ended up doing something you dislike for so long

- **Resentment** towards others whom you consider take from you, without giving back

- **The realisation** your life currently revolves around keeping others happy

- **Poor motivation**, energy and concentration

- **Extreme** mood swings

- **Finding fault** in more things/people than is usual

- **Depressive**, or even suicidal thoughts

- **Insomnia**

- **Wondering what** the point or purpose of your life is

All of these symptoms are common amongst those having a mid-life crisis. This can certainly precipitate a heart attack when married with the other symptoms in this section.

A mid-life crisis is the result of emotional overwhelm

This happens when all of your heart's communications suddenly hit home and cause these symptoms, like a tidal wave. Usually, at this point in your life, your head has had almost total control over your body, motivated by The Lunatic Gene. Fortunately, your body is very resilient and was able to adapt. Consequently, your heart's messages were not sufficient for the judgements of your head to understand your life could be magical, if only you were to listen to your heart's message. Unfortunately, the resilience of your body, combined with the fear of what positive change may bring, can cause extensive periods of wasted life.

If you do not love your life, then what is the point?

Are you here to serve others to the detriment of yourself, or are you here to serve yourself first, so you may serve others better? Is it not more selfless to be self-ish first?

Think about this question.

For a while...

How are your family relationships right now?

Strained close family relationships are a huge symptom of heart disease. The Lunatic Gene comes out to play with gusto in this domain. Without any of my opinions on this subject, think about this: your parents gave you life. If you do not appreciate this, how can you have a healthy heart in this moment?

I know this may not be easy for everyone. From my experience in nursing, family relationships are possibly the most challenging of life's issues. We will delve into this area in a bit more detail later on in the book. For now, just consider, a healthy heart is eventually able to love anyone and any situation. It is The Lunatic Gene that coerces us into anything else. This takes us to the root cause of heart disease: the one area from which all of the other symptoms stem.

Do you love yourself?

This may not seem a straightforward question for you right now. Here is a test if you are unsure. Stand naked in front of a mirror and tell yourself "I love me". If this comes easily, then you probably have a healthy heart. If not, you are at risk of a heart attack. This is a very simple test to find out if you are at risk of heart disease. Please note: there are also other factors. Being able to stand naked in front of a mirror and love yourself does not, in itself, prevent dis-ease, although it is a huge step in the right direction.

Now we shall look at how The Lunatic Gene causes your head to mess with your heart, as we enter your body's courtroom.

Chapter 5. How Your Head Messes With Your Heart

What is the root cause of disease and The Lunatic Gene?

In order to examine this, we will focus on Heart Disease, as I have some experience in this area. In a sentence: **Heart disease occurs when you seek to rule emotion with logic.** This is due to distortions caused by The Lunatic Gene.

- Your heart loves you.

- Your heart has a message it wants you to hear.

- Your heart feels good when you get the message.

- Your heart is in continuous communication with your head.

- Your heart beats independently of your head.

- Your heart is the muscle and pump that keeps you alive.

- Your heart emits an electrical current which can be measured everywhere on your body.

- Your heart has the power to make you ill, or to make you well.

- Your heart's function is dependent on your head's ability to first understand its truth, and then to act upon it.

- Your heart will eventually attack you if you do not listen to it.

Your emotions reflect your thoughts

Every time you think something, chemicals are released from your brain, which lead to an emotional response. Your heart feels your emotions and reacts to them. Your thoughts cause your emotions, and your heart deals with the effects, sending emotional feedback to your head. When something doesn't feel good - then it generally isn't. At this juncture, you have the choice of thinking about a solution to the situation until it does feel good, or ignoring the feeling and dealing with it later. Ignoring a non-positive feeling is a failure to listen to your heart's message.

Like a courtroom case, each emotion likes a fair trial. When left unresolved, emotions become trapped in your body, like a jail, as they await a fair trial. Dealing with issues later creates a pile of unsolved cases. Masses of unreleased, unresolved emotions, which have become imprisoned in your body, are pending a fair hearing. Your heart wants you to resolve every case in a way that feels good. This can only happen if your head allows it.

Dealing with each case, until completion, is one of the most important things you will ever do

In order to act correctly upon your heart's verdict, you will need to understand how your heart works. For this to happen, it will be necessary to look at the relationship it has with your head and your body. To describe how they inter-relate, we will compare it to a courtroom.

In a courtroom, we have the judge, the jury, the verdict and the consequences (or the sentence)

Everything that happens to you is processed through your head, your heart and your body. Your head is your judge, your heart is your jury and your body is your jail. Your head makes the final judgement on all of the issues in your life. Your heart is always giving its verdict, and your body deals with the consequences. Your heart's (or jury's) verdict is felt through your emotions.

If something feels right, this is generally a sign your jury feels your judge has passed a fair sentence. The feeling of being in love is a classic example. If something doesn't feel right, then it is generally a sign for the judge to listen to more evidence, or for your body's jail to imprison another innocent emotional state. All such innocent victims, or emotions, are locked up in your body, waiting for a retrial. Your body then stores an increasing amount of trapped emotions, usually manifested by fear and judgement, influenced by The Lunatic Gene.

Your judge may not always be fair

Any case closed before your jury feels good leads to another jailed emotion, and another open case. This means the case remains unresolved. Innocent emotions are locked up, trapped in your body, until such cases are reopened. If you judge your jury's verdict as wrong and continue thinking the same thoughts, then a kangaroo court is formed. In this instance, the judge prematurely closes the case, and jails the emotion within your body. Like a dictator's rule, this can be unpopular with others when their opinions are disregarded. When innocent emotions are sent to jail, there is chaos waiting to happen somewhere down the line.

Because your body is resilient, it is able to tolerate this abuse of privilege by the judge, sometimes for several decades. This can manifest in your life as feelings of resentment, ill will, criticism of others, temper tantrums or aches and pains in your body.

How can your judge be so out of touch?

There are many books to explain how your head works, at greater lengths than this. Just read a good book on Neuro-Linguistic Programming (NLP). My aim is not to give you all the details of how your brain (or judge) operates - just to give you a brief overview. Your brain is programmed with the energy and beliefs of others. Of course, you form your own beliefs as well.

Like a computer, when you were a baby your brain was taking in everything programmed into you, without any filters. Family beliefs are often passed on - the good and the not so good. Some examples of less than good beliefs I have discovered in clients have been, "None of the people in our family are ever happy", "You will never be as clever as..." and "You always have to work hard to get what you want". This list is endless.

These are just a few examples of beliefs people can take on board when they are really young, which can manifest into everything they do in life, like a mental prison. Worse still is that these programmes often run unconsciously for most of us, thus guiding our judge to make increasingly unfair decisions.

Let us look at the case of Neesha

Neesha grew up in England after her parents moved here from Asia. For many years, she had ignored the calling of her friends and feelings to be expressive, break rules and boundaries, and explore her sense of adventure. After allowing her beliefs to ignore her heart's calling for her whole life, a marriage was arranged for her. Simultaneously, she had a body (or jail) full of innocent emotions, only wanting her judge to know her jury was not happy.

Her heart did not want to get married to the man in question, and her emotions were continually presenting as fear, hurt, guilt and pain. Each time they presented, another innocent emotion was sent to her body's jail by a judge, who believed it was her duty to please her parents – a direct result of family pattern programming. Despite the numerous verdicts of her jury, her judge decided it was the right thing to do for her family, and that her jury was being irrational. Judgement was passed, the emotions were jailed in her body and she went on to live eight utterly miserable years of married life in fear of what everyone else thought. Her judge continually ruled against the advice of her jury as the same case kept coming to court. Meanwhile, more and more innocent emotions were confined to her body's jail.

A jailbreak just waiting to happen

The body only has a certain limit to how many innocent emotions can be trapped, before it starts to present physical symptoms. Aches, pains, depression and even suicidal thoughts are common, which can manifest into conditions more serious if there is not a review in the court. Back pain, for example, can be a direct manifestation of a perceived lack of support.

Neesha had wanted 'out' from the day she was married, but her judge had always over-ruled her jury – a classic case of head ruling heart. However, the pains in her body, due to the unfair imprisonment of her emotions throughout her life, had led her to increasing pain and a dark depression.

She had contemplated suicide

By this stage, her jury was so fed up with not being listened to by the judge, it had wondered what the point of turning up was. Her heart had no energy due to her Lunatic Gene distorting the message of her heart to her head through the insane filter of her family's beliefs. This manifested into low motivation, lack of appetite and suicidal thoughts. These are classic symptoms of The Lunatic Gene running amok. It was only through receiving professional help that Neesha found the courage to leave her marriage - which enraged her family.

She discovered she had been running a strong programme, which told her she had to do what she was told for the good of the family. However, she felt immeasurably better a few months later, after having moved away from her family. When she found a man to whom she was attracted, it was an incredible breakthrough and, at almost thirty years of age, she had finally discovered how important it was to listen to the verdict of her heart. The case was now closed, after her judge's unfair rule had almost led her to suicide.

Myth buster: There is no such thing as a negative emotion

Negative emotions do not exist. All emotions have a positive intention. It is only the judgement of our head that makes them good or bad. All emotions are there to guide us in our journey of life. If you are feeling something does not feel good, it is a clear indication something needs to change in your life. The more you ignore this, the more the emotion will manifest, until you make the change or die. Seek more evidence or help if something is not feeling good over a period of time – as this is how heart dis-ease occurs.

Your natural state is neutral. The pursuit of emotions you perceive as positive can be highly detrimental to you, if this means other emotions are considered negative. Happiness is not better than sadness – it just feels better. If you are not feeling happy, there is a chance you may feel unhappy. If you pursue a course of action that does not feel good for any considerable length of time, then it is highly likely emotions such as hurt, guilt or fear will be your regular companions.

However, emotions like fear, hurt and anger can be wonderful catalysts towards positive change. To do this, it is important to keep each case open until you *feel* good about it. This may be a decision to cut a person or situation out of your life entirely. Situations you do not deal with, which don't feel good, will not just go away – ever.

Pain is usually a bigger motivator than pleasure

If I were to say you would meet your soul mate and earn a fortune, if you fearlessly pursued the things you loved to do for the rest of your life, would you be likely to do it?

Your head is probably realising if you were happier and doing the things you love, then these outcomes are likely. However, it may well construct a reason why you could not do it right now. In much the same way most smokers realise they would be healthier if they smoked less and might even live longer – this is not a motivating force for most.

Conversely, if you were to find out the person whom you loved the most in the world would leave your life unless you spoke your truth, ate a healthier diet and/or exercised more, whilst doing what you loved, is there anything which would stop you making the changes?

For this reason, emotions such as anger, fear and hurt can be your best friends. When you realise most human beings are more motivated by pain than pleasure, it makes sense that your heart needs to sometimes re-present verdicts that do not feel good. This is your heart's attempt to guide you to a better place. We will discuss this further in chapter nine.

People who feel stuck in jobs or relationships, who do not feel good for years at a time, are strong candidates for a heart attack

A heart attack is the ultimate rebellion of your jury. The spark for this can be a jailbreak from the numerous innocent victims of years, sometimes decades, of autocratic rule from an unreasonable judge. Ultimately, if your heart stops working, your body dies and your judge has no courtroom in which to operate. It makes no sense: The Lunatic Gene rarely does.

Your heart can survive without your head

It may not be an ideal situation to be brain-dead, but your heart and body can survive without your head. Of course, I do not include those who have faced the guillotine or beheading in this equation, just the fact our brains are not needed for our bodies to survive. Your heart does not need your brain to keep it beating or perform its function. Conversely, your brain is totally dependent on the smooth functioning of your heart. For this reason it is essential to listen to your heart, listen to your jury and listen to your body. Failure to do so will almost certainly result in early death.

On that bombshell, we will now look at how your relationships affect your heart.

Chapter 6. Examine Your Relationships

Your relationships are all like branches from a tree. Family dynamics can change, friends come and go and everything else is a constant roller coaster of change. Your relationships with food, work, time, exercise and money are all different branches of the same tree. All are interconnected and come from the same root.

Two beautiful branches do not make a beautiful tree

It surprises me that when heart disease rears its head, the areas of diet and exercise are always targeted as the lead focus for change by many experts on the subject. Of course, diet and exercise are important, but they are symptoms of something far deeper. This is why people who go on strict diets sometimes still watch their cholesterol levels rise, while others have heart attacks whilst exercising.

At the end of your life, there will be two things that suddenly become really important

I have guided people through their final moments and witnessed many interesting things. Some people suffer incredibly, defying the death sentence doctors gave them and living days, weeks, months or even years longer than was estimated. This extra time is frequently not quality time. Often people will suffer and start to question many things about their lives.

Others will go to sleep peacefully and never wake up. Witnessing such serenity at the end of life is a beautiful thing. My grandad, at the age of 94, had the whole hospital ward laughing the night before he went to sleep and never woke up again. Unfortunately, as a nurse I did not get to witness this very often, because of two factors.

The first factor: family relationships

I have witnessed this time and time again in hospitals. When people are facing death there are two recurrent themes that come up. Family relationships are one of them. Any close, family issues will generally represent during the dying process, and lead to further suffering if still unresolved. On a large number of occasions, I have seen people cling to life until a certain relative visits, and then die shortly afterwards. Sometimes the patient is unconscious for days, yet still waits until a certain relative visits, before dying.

Easier said than done

When dealing with family challenges, it is all too easy to give good advice. The fact is, resolving family relationships can be a life-long journey for some, and even then it may not yield a positive result. This can be a very deep rabbit hole, and it is understandable people may not be ready to face whatever comes up. Emotions like pride, anger and hurt can be powerful barriers when your focus is not right.

However, those same emotions can also be powerful catalysts of change. All it takes is enough pain to force you to confront your family relationship issues. When this happens, you may well be in for a roller-coaster ride. Any negative thoughts you have about others will ultimately affect you the most. Personally, I would always recommend that you get professional help when working through family issues, if they have been recurrent for more than six months. Make sure you feel well supported through this process, and you feel certain you are ready to do whatever it takes to get positive results.

I sometimes hear about people being in therapy for years at a time. Personally, I think this is not ideal. A good therapist will raise the bar, and get results for you as quickly as you feel you can get them. If you believe your issues are worthy of years of therapy, then by all means pay the price. However, time is the biggest price you'll pay. If your family member dies before you reach resolution, then the process gets a little more complicated.

This is not to say you will not reach a great resolution, only it takes a very skilled intervention to help you to swiftly resolve family issues around dead family members. In my experience, nothing is quite as powerful as being able to talk through issues with family members, and give them a hug at the end of it, especially if this is something you haven't done for several years. I have personal experience in this area.

Having the courage to work through your low points in life is one of the biggest challenges you will ever face

Be brave, be bold and get help if you find yourself stuck in the emptiness - from someone who has been there on more than one occasion. This is my advice if you find yourself resonating with this. Now we will look at the single most important relationship in your life.

Chapter 7. The Most Important Relationship in Your Life

There are two ways to reach resolution in all of your relationships

The first way is to deal with each relationship individually. One by one address every family member, friend, ex-friend, partner/lover, boss, work colleague and random stranger who has ever upset you. This is the slow, painful, damage-limitation method many people tend to adopt, which usually depends on other people being reasonable. In the same way fire-fighters work, you will always be waiting for the next fire to start. I do not recommend this approach.

The second way is to work on the only relationship that really matters in your life: the one you have with yourself. If you improve your relationship with yourself, every other relationship in your life will improve, as if by magic. This is because all other relationships in your life stem from the same point – you.

What happens when you don't love yourself?

Having a loving relationship with yourself allows you to see everyone else from the same focal point, which is love. Not having a loving relationship with yourself means, in every relationship you ever have, you will swing between two poles. This is not to say you will be a pole-dancer, just your perception will have two main focal points. Not loving yourself will move you between loving someone more than you love yourself, and loving someone less than you love yourself. This is how polarity is reached in your relationships.

When you love someone more than you love yourself, you cut yourself off from your power. This is not love based on flow and connection, it is a love based on addiction and neediness. You know the symptoms: numerous unanswered calls or texts, blame, guilt and disempowerment involved in each interaction, threats of suicide or self-harming and a feeling of being trapped - to name but a few.

If you want to be loved in the same way you love your partner, it is necessary to love yourself at least as much as you love them. When you do not, you can hurt yourself, and you depend on your partner to love you more than you love yourself. This is likely to attract someone who is either hoping to rescue, change or abuse you. Things may not appear this way at first, but they will certainly manifest this way with time.

To balance this in your life you will find fault with others. Any action or behaviour you don't like will usually be criticised, often without the person you are finding fault with getting to hear the accusations. This can also manifest as an addiction to hearing bad news, which is abundant on our airwaves and news reports. There will always be someone less loving, more corrupt or less deserving of love than you (from your perspective). From this place of judgement you can find balance, whilst loving some people more, and others less, than you love yourself.

When you find yourself being critical or judgemental about others regularly, you have lost love with yourself

Finding fault in others is a very human thing to do. In situations like murder, rape and violence, it can be particularly challenging to not find fault. Often, we do not even know why we do it, we just do. This is hardly surprising when we take a look at what themes are commonly presented to us via media sources.

War, death, violence, destruction, shock, devastation and theft are far more likely to make the lead story of the news or the front page of a newspaper than are peace, harmony, love, resolution and hope. With images of models who are fat-free and made-up to look too good to be true, it is no wonder so many people have issues about how they look and whether they can be loved. Our focus is constantly being drawn towards what isn't working on the planet, rather than what is.

You become what you focus upon the most

Since an early age, the focus of the world media has been on what doesn't work. So many people delight in the misfortune of others, because it makes them feel just a little bit better about themselves. This is why soap operas are so popular. Photos of celebrities showing cellulite, going to jail or walking into rehabilitation are big news, because they help us to avoid the real issue: how do you feel about yourself?

If you loved yourself fully and completely, it would not be an issue to you what anybody else's faults were. You would be able to talk through and address anything not working for you, loving anything and anyone else, or simply be empowered enough to walk away from anyone or anything which wasn't benefiting you. You would realise those who challenge you are just using you as a sounding board to highlight the area(s) of their own lives which are deficient.

We do not see the world how it is: we see it how we are

If you can remember having a feeling of excitement, the same excitement you had when you found out about your first ever date, then you will know what I mean. As a ten-year-old boy, I was overweight. I didn't really love myself very much at all. All of the reminders from other school children about my weight excess just helped to drill home I could not be loved. Every comment hurt, and life could be challenging at times.

When I asked a girl in my class if she would be my girlfriend and she said 'yes', things appeared very different. I did not even know what having a girlfriend entailed, except for the jubilation I felt as I realised there was someone who didn't find me unlovable. No comments would register, other than the good ones. Nothing was going to stop me feeling fantastic. I could not even muster the thoughts to dislike those who liked to call me names. Quite simply, the world was a wonderful place to me, as I found myself bursting with excitement, elation and happiness.

Conversely, when I was told the mother of the girl in question had informed her she was too young to have a boyfriend, and we couldn't be together, the world nearly ended for me. Suddenly I was able to find fault in almost everything and everyone again.

Maybe you have had days like this

When life smiles upon you, it instantly moves you to a place that feels great. From this place the same actions, comments and words of others will usually be perceived differently when you are feeling this way. Comments intended to be hurtful can often be laughed at, accidents generally will not affect you as much, and potentially bad news just does not register in the same way. People who appear angry or sad are just off your radar.

When you are not feeling as if life is smiling upon you, the world becomes a darker place. From here, everything that is 'not great' gets escalated. The slightest remark could upset you, and things appear to be working against you as your perception changes. The same actions, accidents, comments and gestures you could laugh about in your empowered state now become issues that need to be dealt with. If anyone has the audacity to show up happy, then you may feel resentment towards them. From here, you are placed back in a fire-fighting, judgemental mode, and will need to be alert constantly.

Taking back control

When you start to love yourself better, you are able to perceive things differently. This does not mean the events in your life change - only the way you process them. Ask yourself how you usually react when a challenge presents. Phrases like, "This always happens to me", "Just my luck", or "I should have guessed something like this would happen" can be less than productive.

Questions like: "What is the lesson in this situation?" "How can I learn and grow from this?" or "What can I do to improve this situation right now?" can help. Although they may not always instantly yield better results, they will allow you to shift your focus towards a more positive outcome. Making a conscious effort to take deeper breaths will also help. We will discuss this in more detail later.

Disclaimer

In writing this, I offer you a possible template as to why we do what we do, and how to change it. This is not to say you must agree with it or it is easy to implement all of the time. I sometimes still find myself being critical of others and experiencing strained relationships. I still have to wrestle with my Lunatic Gene occasionally, before we decide to dance!

We are all human, and it is not always easy to let go of events and situations that appear unfair or unjust. Anger can be a wonderful catalyst for change. Allowing people who have not been getting great results in their lives to access anger can be one of the best things ever. Anger motivates, and often causes change. However, unresolved anger continuing for an extended period of time has been shown to not only fatigue your body, causing restlessness and mood swings, it can also harden your arteries.

Get to know yourself better

In order to improve your relationship with yourself, it is necessary to get to know yourself better. You may well be wondering how you can do this. Unfortunately, most of us will probably die with no idea of who we really are. There is so much mystery about life, our origins and the point of our existence; it can be overwhelming at times.

I am not going to get into a deep and philosophical discussion on the point of life just yet. Instead, I will offer you a tool I learnt during my nurse training that can improve your awareness of who you really are. I am going to upset a few people with my next statement, but I believe in being honest: much of my nurse training was boring and largely irrelevant to me at the time.

I know there will be loud cries from my former trainers about the importance of what we learnt and, in fairness, I can see the bigger picture now in learning health care systems, government policy and the components of reading a research paper. However, at the time all I wanted to know was how to do my job, take observations, make sense of them, get on with the staff and keep my patients alive. I wanted to learn practical skills, not theory. My first few shifts as a student nurse found me badly lacking in the necessary skills to help the qualified nurses.

A breath of fresh air in our nurse training

Every now and then we would have trainers sent in to teach us various components of nursing, personal development and hospital policy. These were largely uninspiring for me. Then, one day two ladies walked in and revealed 'Johari's window'. I had my newspaper ready at the back of the class. It was usual for me to read it surreptitiously just after each class started, to pass away time, as certain, boring tutors rambled on. I was not a model student.

However, when our guests started talking about Johari's window, I found myself intrigued

Johari's window was named after Joseph Luft and Harry Ingham in 1955, and used as a cognitive psychological tool to help people better understand their interpersonal communication and relationships. It comprised of a window, with four panes. The horizontal axis of the window represents what others know about us and the vertical axis represents what we know about ourselves.

When this tool was used in clinical practice, a list of adjectives would be placed in front of someone, and also separately with their friends. Traits like happy, caring, lazy, inspired, moody, motivated, boring and loving would be used. Depending on the similarities and differences in traits chosen by the individual and their friends, a profile was formed.

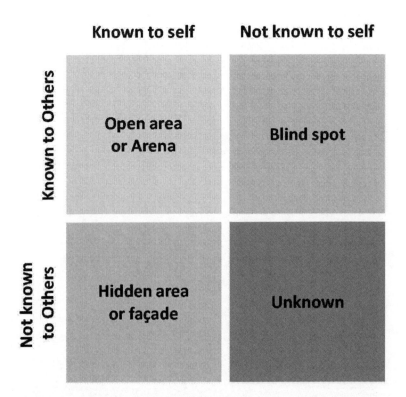

The Johari Window Model

The Four Panes

The top-left section of Johari's window represents the part of ourselves we and others see. Aspects like our name, where we live, whether you are generally happy, sad, caring or self-centred, and other commonly known things.

The bottom-left section represents the traits you know about yourself but which nobody else knows. These are generally the things you feel you could not possibly tell anyone else. These aspects are what you hide from the world.

The top-right section is all of the traits other people perceive about you which are outside of your awareness. These are out of your awareness because nobody has told you about them, and you haven't asked. Things here can be anything from quirky habits, like facial ticks or words you use regularly - without realising it - or the fact they find you an inspiration - or even a fool.

The bottom-right pane is the realm of the unknown. This is the area of you nobody knows. Certain situations can only be speculated upon, but if they really happened, you have no idea what you would do. An example of such areas could be: how would you react if a stranger pointed a loaded gun at you? If you were put in a situation where you had to kill a stranger to save someone who you loved: could you do it? Would you compromise your principles for a million pounds? These are just a few examples of things that could be in this area. All of these areas you can speculate upon, but you will never really know unless they were to happen. Many people claim to be highly moral in speculative situations, although I'm not so sure this would stand up in a real situation!

By expanding your awareness of one section, all of the others shift in size

The two areas you can shift to increase your awareness are the top-right and the bottom-left sections. What others know that you don't, and what you know that others don't, are the two areas you can work on. By doing this you will get a bigger picture of who you really are. This is done through being more open and honest, and through seeking feedback more regularly.

When I decided to discover more about who I really am it happened by consciously focusing on the two areas in question. The first thing I did was go to some of my closest friends, many of whom have known me for over a decade, and asked them how they would describe me, why they valued my friendship and what specific areas they felt I needed to develop. At first this felt a bit strange, but I was genuinely shocked at the feedback I received.

All of the things I did naturally, such as being a good listener, being calm in a crisis, loving to laugh and having fun, I had taken for granted. Yet, in friend after friend these things came up repeatedly, helping me to realise these were my key skills. I also gave my friends the opportunity to be honest about what aspects they thought I could improve upon in order to be a better friend. This is the area that can be the most uncomfortable of all, yet rewarding.

Finding out that many of my friends perceived I was too generous for my own good, and I didn't look after myself nearly as much as I looked after others, was tough to face - but it was true. I did not look after myself nearly as well as I looked after everyone else. I did not love myself. It took the brutal honesty of my friends to make me face this fact. This only happened when I gave them permission to be honest.

Giving feedback can be a tricky subject

When you ask someone for their opinion, it is a really good idea to learn how to receive it in a way that will inspire them to do it again. Some people will give you feedback whether you ask for it or not. This is a completely different area, and how you respond to that is a separate issue.

It makes me wonder sometimes, when people ask me for my opinion on something, then clearly not like my response. This can cause defensiveness, and has been known to upset people. If you are going to ask someone for an opinion - be open to receive it. If you really mean for someone to give their opinion only if it is good one, then make sure you let them know that.

The incorrect way to take feedback

If someone gives you an opinion after you have asked for it, and you start to justify yourself, get defensive and disagree with the person in question, then what do you think are the chances of them being honest with you again? If you have done this even once to any of your friends, then they have already learnt to moderate their opinion based on what you are really looking for. Because they are your friends, they want you to like them. If they feel being honest will stop you from liking them, it is possible they will stop being completely honest.

Can you handle the truth?

Real friends will never do this deliberately to deceive you, they just do it because they are giving you what they think you need to hear at the time. Yes, there are friends who will be brutally honest, regardless what you say or do. I have found such friends are priceless.

The correct way to take feedback

If you have asked for feedback from someone, then it pays to understand the following things:

- **It is just** their opinion and not necessarily true

- **It takes courage** for a friend to be really honest, when it could be perceived as criticism

- **If you want** people to be honest with you when you ask for their opinions, then it is your duty to make them feel comfortable as they do it

- **It is always** your choice whether to believe, or act upon, anything you are told

- **Your real friends** are always working from what they perceive are your best interests

- **The more** feedback you get, the faster you are likely to develop

The most important factor of all when taking feedback after you have asked for it is to thank the person at the end of it. Saying, "Thank you for your feedback" is the only thing necessary. If you have any questions beyond this, ask them. Feedback is neither right nor wrong: it is just feedback. Learning how to accept it graciously will improve all of your relationships and skyrocket your self-awareness.

Tips on giving feedback

Feedback is best delivered as part of a feedback sandwich. For example, say something you like, give the area that needs improvement and then give something else that is positive to finish with. By sandwiching things that do not work between those that do, it is possible to get your message across in a way which is not only highly effective, but also leaves the person feeling good.

I was once at a training course where I was learning presentation skills. After one exercise, my facilitator told me I was one of the most promising students in the class, before telling me my posture could be improved, along with my tonality, hand gestures and content. My presentation was broken down into small pieces and I was effectively told I was grossly under-performing on this particular exercise. Afterwards, I was told, with a little work, I had the potential to make a living through public speaking.

It was one of the best dressings-down I have ever received

Even though many aspects of my presentation had been brought into question, I left feeling good about what I'd just heard, and really motivated to work on the areas which needed to be improved.

In all of your communications, learning how to sandwich your feedback so that it starts and ends on a positive note, will be far more likely to yield positive outcomes. Aligned with a "thank you for your feedback" as the only response to give after feedback has been given, you will likely experience your relationships moving up to another level.

If you were not quite ready for that, the next chapter may well help.

Chapter 8. Life Feels Better When it is For-Giving

There are many possible reasons why life may not be working for you all of the time. You will be challenged: you will be probed and you will react - whether you like it or not. The Lunatic Gene will mess with your head in many different ways, but your heart is there to help you to navigate even the most challenging situations in your life. This is not an easy thing to do, and any steps in the right direction are a good place to start.

When you find yourself caught in thoughts of rage, injustice or revenge, it is not always easy to quickly change the way you feel. Indeed, there are people out there who will abuse your good nature, steal from you, fight you, beat you and not care about the consequences for you. It may not be right, it may not be fair, but it is the way life can be sometimes, and how it has been for as long as records recall.

Just imagine, some people are given weapons and told to fight, risking their lives every day. People are killing each other around the world, whilst others are dying of starvation. Nothing is certain in your life, except death. Should you choose to do so, you could spend a lifetime pondering the injustice in the world. This is a choice many people veer towards, because life can be tough. To cap it all, you get to die at the end of it, and you'll never know when or how until that day arrives. Meanwhile, your Lunatic Gene feeds off your neuroses, playing havoc with your emotions.

Now we have the good news out of the way!

There is an alternative. Let go of anything that doesn't feel good. Start by working out what doesn't feel good for you right now, and addressing it until you feel better. So many people reach the end of their lives regretting the things they didn't do while they had the chance. The most powerful tool I know for this is for-giving. Anger, resentment, guilt, fear and pain can all happen when your head is for-getting that your heart is for-giving.

Just the word 'forgiving' is powerful. When you give to someone, you can only guarantee you will feel happy and energised about it if you are also prepared to forgive. Whilst many people may well be grateful for any kind acts you might bestow upon them, there will be others who may take your kindness for granted, or appear less than gracious for your good deeds.

As long as you retain your intention as positive, then all of your acts of giving will positively enhance your wellbeing, your mood and your life. Being able to forgive those whom you feel have done you wrong is the fastest and most powerful path to a healthier heart that I know of. The highest form of revenge is indifference.

Learn from masters

When you are faced with a testing situation, the stress on your heart is compounded. Ill thoughts can be harnessed and used to attack, or they can be alchemised into inspirational lessons to help your friends and family grow faster, and to be inspired by you. To be able to do this takes time, training and practice. To do this you will need to learn from a master.

Many of life's real lessons are so much easier to understand logically than to act upon emotionally. If you have ever watched or read 'A

Christmas Carol', then you will know the feeling of when Scrooge finally *gets it*, and runs through the streets on Christmas morning looking to mend his ways.

His nephew plays the ultimate forgiving role. Each year he asks Scrooge to Christmas dinner. Despite the hostile responses, he is never despondent and always sees the good in Scrooge, even though this is a major challenge for everyone else. Could you do this?

Your thoughts are like boomerangs

The simplest explanation of how your heart and energy work would be to see your thoughts as boomerangs. Every single thought you have about anyone else, whether you tell anyone or not, comes straight back at you and impacts your body.

Because your energy follows your thoughts, every single thought has a direct impact upon you. You may not believe this at the moment, but think about it for a while. Most people I know get upset when they find out someone has said something unfavourable about them. However, this does not usually stop those same people from saying unfavourable things about others, even when those others don't even get a chance to hear their accusers directly.

Do unto others as you would like done to you

Now, I'm not suggesting if you suddenly get the urge to never say anything critical about anyone or anything again, that people will stop finding fault in you. This is not a likely outcome. However, if you make a conscious decision to not criticise others, unless it is to their face, you will find you will be less affected by the second-hand opinions of others.

During some of my workshops I ask, "If every thought you had, and word you spoke, were collected and delivered to those whom you talked or thought about, how many of you would be happy for this to happen?" Very few people ever put their hands up.

How would your thoughts and words change if you knew, for sure, the people you were thinking or talking about would find out exactly what you really thought about them?

I worked night shifts for over ten of my thirteen years in nursing. During this period, I would frequently have the time to sit and listen to my work colleagues. So often, I would hear tales about how a person had done something bad and someone should do something about it. For several years, I would tolerate this as part of the job, despite feeling my life-force drain when it started to happen.

Eventually, I adopted a strategy that allowed me to move through the night without having to listen to such criticism. With one simple question my life changed. When colleagues would start criticising other members of staff I would ask them: "Have you spoken with the person involved?"

Almost always the answer was no. I would then say, "Are you going to?" Almost always the answer to this question would be no. At this point, I would answer, "So why are you telling me?" This trail of questions was often asked with a smile on my face, as I knew what the answers would be. I learnt to become a Devil's Advocate occasionally during my time as a nurse. This made the role more fun, and landed me in some very interesting situations.

The fact is, most people give out what they don't like to take in

So many would think nothing of being critical about others, but would be mortally wounded if anyone said the same things about them. I have done this myself on numerous occasions. The only difference now is that if I find myself thinking ill thoughts about others, I often speak to them about it before telling anyone else. If I feel my judgement may be clouded, which high emotion can often cause, I may first run a proposed course of action by a trusted friend. From here, I will either be told I am being unreasonable, calm down and change my mind, or go straight to the person in question and tell them how I feel. Do you do this?

Know who your real friends are

Real friends are not just there to support you and agree with everything you do. Real friends will know when it's time to say you are out of line when you do something that does not serve you. I have been there on numerous occasions and am very grateful for a network of friends who are used to holding me to a higher standard.

If you are in a bad place, or facing a testing situation where you are about to say something to someone whom you believe has crossed the line, then it often pays to tell one trusted friend who has a track record of telling you when they feel your motivation may not be right. Having a friend like this is pure gold when you are not feeling great.

Pause for thought

When you find yourself in a highly emotional state, it can help greatly to pause if you find yourself about to deliver a verdict that may hurt other people and, ultimately, you too. Revenge and retaliation may well feel justified in a given moment but they always have repercussions which may not be particularly pleasant.

Ho'oponopono

This is the ancient Hawaiian practice of reconciliation and forgiveness. It is defined in the Hawaiian dictionary as, 'mental cleansing: family conferences in which relationships were set right through prayer, discussion, confession, repentance, mutual restitution and forgiveness'.

Quite simply, this process works by taking any situation in your life, which is not currently working, relaxing and repeating the mantra; "I'm sorry. Please forgive me. I love you. Thank you." These words have a healing energy, and if repeated often enough can change the way you feel about any situation in your life.

I strongly suggest that you stop and practice this now around a certain situation. Whilst the actions of others may well be unreasonable, the only way you can guarantee resolution is to empower yourself to resolve this on your own.

Chapter 9. Your Emotional Guidance System (EGS)

Before you can connect to what you want, it is essential to feel what you don't want

It becomes easy to live a non heart-based life when you don't know what the real problem is. Some people are so disconnected from their real feelings that they have not felt enough pain to motivate them to change their lives. When I talk about pain, I mean emotional pain, as much as physical pain. Pain is not always easy to deal with, but is often necessary to motivate you and create positive and sustainable change. Being a stubborn character with a high tolerance for pain, like myself, has been a huge challenge in this respect. It took me a lot of pain and years to realise this lesson. I'm hoping to save you some of the suffering involved in this approach.

However, because your judge can become skilled at not dealing with perceived negative emotions, motivation for change can remain one elusive step away. Allied with The Lunatic Gene guiding you towards personal turmoil, this can be a rocky road. If you have ever felt emptiness, where you know something is missing from your life, but you don't know what it is, then you know what I'm talking about. Only through facing your pain, fear, anger and hurt, and staying with those feelings for long enough, are you likely to motivate yourself enough for positive change to occur. Meditation can be good in such instances.

E-Motion = Energy in Motion

We are emotional animals. We act emotionally and justify logically. This is how we are hard-wired. You cannot control laughter or tears for your whole life, you can only tell a story as to why it happens. If you have ever been head-over-heels in love, then you will know what I'm talking about. Sometimes, there is just no logical explanation for what we do. Anger and injustice are no different.

It is easy to pass judgement on the actions of others. However, understanding the emotional state of someone gives a broader perspective of why they do what they do. Ask yourself, if someone threatened one of your close family members, would you be able to act logically in such a moment?

Maybe you could. However, many would not be able to, and when we feel our loved-ones are under threat, then logic often takes a back seat. Road rage is a good example of how our emotions can rule. Put someone behind the wheel of a car and see how they react to bad driving from others. This can bring out the more emotional, instinctive urges and frustrations.

Discovering your Emotional Guidance System (EGS)

Your EGS is your heart's sat-nav to leading a happier, healthier life. All emotions are caused by what you are thinking about, and have a cycle of approximately 90 seconds. They are, like a fuel gauge, only a temporary measure of where you are. Becoming aware of how you feel on a moment-to-moment basis gives you the option of thinking something better, changing the chemical released in your brain as a result, and moving effortlessly to a better place. That is the theory. The practice takes focus, concentration and effort in order to become aware of how you feel more often.

Rather than living life through logic, which is often the result of other people's thinking, you can be guided to a life of happiness and fulfilment. To do this, it is essential you tune into your heart and EGS

- changing your thinking and/or doing something different if something doesn't feel good.

There is no such thing as a negative emotion

I have mentioned this before, and have no hesitation about mentioning it again. *This aspect is crucial to you living in alignment with the needs of your heart.* This may not always be sweetness and light. Sometimes your heart will demand you do something different to feel better. Remember: there is no such thing as a negative emotion!

Susan was used to running her family home. For over twenty years, she had cooked for everyone, cleaned-up after everyone, and did whatever she could to help her husband and two sons. Over time, she was starting to feel taken for granted and felt nobody really looked after her. This manifested in an empty feeling, accompanied by hurt and low motivation.

One day, these repetitive thoughts she had been having for the past few years coincided with a crippling headache. For three days, she was left to suffer, and no medications were working. Meanwhile, her complaints fell on deaf ears from the rest of her family, who still expected to be fed and cleaned-up after.

Susan had been running a grossly unfair, kangaroo court within her body for many years, and the jailbreak was happening. Like a pressure cooker, she was about to explode. It was her eldest son who happened to be in the wrong place at the wrong time when this happened. Just a simple statement like, "I'm hungry. What time is dinner ready?" was enough to spark an emotional explosion.

Susan let her son have it with both barrels. He was accused of taking her for granted, being lazy, selfish, uncaring, inconsiderate and thoughtless. Years of frustration spilled out and Susan appeared to have no control over it. She had always been so accommodating, kind and reasonable to her family, so this was a shock for her son.

Whilst Susan felt bad afterwards about what she had said and done, it sparked a series of events causing her family to start changing their habits around the house. Her husband started buying her more gifts and making her drinks. Her sons started cooking and cleaning to help out and they all spent more time doing things as a family.

Whilst a jailbreak is not ideal, it often gets results. Emotions need to be acknowledged, and change needs to occur if things are not working for you. In Susan's case, she had spent years ignoring how she felt, as old, family programming about it being a woman's job to run the house kept her feeling unhappy in her heart. Her head told her this was what she had to do, based on what her mother had told her.

Good outcomes can come from the most unexpected sources

When such emotional outbursts happen, there is a Western tendency to then feel guilty about acting so 'out of character'. The fact is, denying your emotions is the real problem. This is really you acting out of character. However, because so many people do this for most of their lives, they do not realise the real you is the part that does stand up to injustice. The real you does express how you feel in a way that gets positive results. The real you is a constant calling from within, wanting you to feel better.

If you can feel the real you burning from within, then you know what you need to do. The only question is: Do you have the courage and motivation to do it?

If the situation in question has been on your mind repeatedly for a number of minutes, then you have time on your side, and you will act when the time feels right. If the situation has been on your mind for a number of months, then it is likely you have been experiencing certain physical symptoms along the way. Headaches, pains in your body, indigestion and insomnia are just some potential symptoms of a mini jailbreak. If the situation in question has been on your mind for a number of years you are most certainly at risk of a more serious illness developing. A heart attack is just one possibility. Amongst the others are cancer and strokes.

There is no way of cushioning the blow

Your heart wants you to feel better at any given moment. When you are feeling positive, then you are generally in alignment with your EGS and your heart is happier and healthier. When you are not feeling positive, then your heart is demanding justice from within your body's courtroom. Until you address this, the call will get louder until you make the change(s) necessary, or you die.

To do this, you need to know how you feel about certain situations

Like the art of map reading, there is no point in being able to read a map if you do not know where your starting point is. In order to get yourself to a better place, it is essential you know exactly where you are now. To do this you will need to honestly assess how you feel about your life right now.

It is normal to not feel good about a situation, because it is a feeling and a call for change. Being able to feel your way through a situation is your way of discovering where you are on the map. You can then start to negotiate a route to a better place. This may not happen easily, but it will happen as long as you set your intention for it to happen.

To do this it will be helpful to start thinking about a bigger picture.

We will look at this in the next chapter.

Chapter 10. Examining The Bigger Picture of Your Life

"Champions aren't made in gyms. Champions are made from something that they have deep inside them – a desire, a dream, a vision. They have to have the skill, and the will. But the will must be stronger than the skill."

Muhammad Ali

I mentioned near the beginning of the book that recurrent themes arose for people at the end of their lives. This is the one that matters the most. This is the difference that makes a difference. It has the potential to change everything in your life. Before we get to this we will look at the two vantage points of any situation.

Do you like the details or the big picture?

Now we have had a look at some of the things The Lunatic Gene can do to sabotage your heart, we will take a step out and look at a bigger picture. In life, you will find yourself moving between two planes on any given subject: the small details or the big picture. We each have a preference and this may change in different areas of your life.

Although I generally prefer the big picture in all I do, there will be times where it is the small details that really make a difference. For example, learning search engine optimisation (SEO) requires special attention to the small details. Much as I didn't like having to learn such things, I found it fascinating to find out how it works. At times, as a nurse, the details were often the difference between life and death. Give the wrong drug on a bad day and somebody could die. Whilst extreme, I've seen this happen - not by me, I hasten to add!

If someone asks me how I am doing, I will usually sum it up in a sentence, or even just one word, because I am a big picture thinker and I like to cut to the chase. You may notice when you ask some people how they are doing, you then get a step-by-step account of everything happening in their lives - right then. These are your detail people.

Learning about logical levels gives you a broader view of a situation

Problems can very rarely be solved on the same logical level they are created. Let us imagine an example. You are just about to go to work and your car won't start. At this level, you have a car problem. The car problem will not fix itself, so you will have to move up or down a level to deal with this problem. By moving down in logical levels, a mechanic may well point out the problem is with the petrol tank. One level further down, it could be a problem that it is leaking.

Knowing the detail of this problem may help to fix the car, but it may not solve the bigger issue. Only by moving up through the logical levels of a problem will you solve the real issue. The bigger level problem, in this case, is one of transportation. The transportation problem could be solved by fixing the car, walking or getting another means of transport to work. It may be possible to leave the car and get a lift to work from a colleague, or take public transport. The car can be fixed, but not in time for you to get to work that day. Transportation is the higher level of the problem.

One level further up from this is the reason you need transportation, which could be to go to work. At this level, finding a job closer to home could solve the problem - should it happen again.

As we go higher up the levels, we ask what purpose work serves. This is usually money. It is here we find a problem paradox. You need to work to get money, and it will cost money to fix the car and possibly require time off work. The next level of the problem is the reason money is important. This could be something like survival or having the freedom to do what you want. In this instance, starting a home-based business may well be the bigger-picture solution. But would this pay enough?

If you were to ask yourself to what purpose more freedom would serve you, it could end up with something like happiness. The purpose of happiness may well lead to love, which would be the goal of all of your actions and decisions. In this instance, working in a job you didn't love would be paradoxical, and be a potential disaster for your heart. If this was the case, then the car costing money to run and fix could lead to further unhappiness, placing strain on relationships and moving you away from love. When this paradox occurs, your Lunatic Gene comes out to play havoc with your head and heart.

All levels of the problem lead to love, or a lack of it. At the highest level of a problem it is easier to solve issues in a way that all serve the same purpose. When you realise this, anything not leading you to love is an indicator something may not be working. Are you getting the drift?

Let us summarise the levels of this problem

Love

I

Happiness

I

Freedom

I

Money

I

Work

I

Transport

I

Car

I

Petrol Tank

I

Leak

The presenting problem was the car not starting. This is the level most people focus on. They panic, call someone who can fix it, and focus on the fact they may be late to work. This usually involves a financial cost, provokes a stress response and sets up the day badly. The mechanic then arrives and helps you to go down in the logical levels of the problem. You now move from understanding your car would not start to knowing there was a leak in the petrol tank. Then you weigh up the cost and time-delay involved in fixing your car, caught at the logical level of transport. This is generally not a happy experience and is counter-productive to your ultimate goal, which in this case would be love.

Your ultimate goal may well be different, but there will always be a highest value motivating your mood and actions. This is often unconscious, as many people do not take time to discover what their highest value is. This is an area I often help people with.

What if you chose to move up in the logical levels of the problem and find a bigger picture solution?

If the reason you needed the car to start is to work and earn money, in order to be able to spend more time with your children, why not start thinking differently? In this case, the car breaking down could have the power to change your life entirely, in a very positive way. Rather than just getting frustrated, it could be the final straw in sparking a much greater desire within you.

For what purpose?

The above question is your access route to moving up in the logical levels of a problem. For what purpose do you need a car? In this case, a car is needed to get to work. For what purpose do you need to go to work? Money, etc., etc., as the process continues.

Within any problem, by asking yourself what the purpose is, you automatically move yourself into the bigger picture. To move down in logical levels and get the details, the question to ask is, "How, specifically?"

If you take every issue you have ever had and move up in logical levels, it will usually lead you to exactly the same place. Such a place may be anything from survival or existence, to happiness or love. Whatever the end destination to your question of purpose, it will be far more motivating than the average everyday problems most of us can get stuck in. Your ability to work productively with The Lunatic Gene is in direct proportion to your ability to see all of the logical levels of any situation, and stay connected with your highest value on this chain.

How do you discover your ultimate motivation?

In simple terms, you keep asking the question, "For what purpose?" This will take you to your top logical level. From this point, it is your job to find a cause to align you with this. However, it is easy to get stuck, or confused, if you have no experience of going through this process. For this reason, I would advise seeking a skilled therapist who has trained in logical levels of therapy. Most Neuro-Linguistic Programming (NLP) trained professionals will be able to help you with this.

Alternatively, ask yourself what you would do with your life if you could achieve anything you wanted, and could guarantee it would happen in the future. Focusing on what you want when the chips are down is the best way to free yourself from this situational lunacy.

Think big

My experience of conducting this exercise is that most people will not allow themselves to think very big. In this case, ask yourself: who is the person you admire most, alive or dead, real or made-up? It could be a character from a book, a great world leader or a person you know. Make sure the person you choose has exceeded anything you think humanly possible for you to do right now.

Think why

When you have found your figure of inspiration, ask yourself why you admire them so much. Is it because they repeatedly overcame adversity? Is it because they showed great courage and changed the course of the entire planet? Is it because they achieved something that would be considered impossible to most? Maybe it's because they had more fun than you could possibly imagine.

How would you change the world if you knew you could?

Now is an opportunity to turn all of your challenges, frustrations and complaints into focus. What would you change in your world if you knew you could? How would you choose to impact the entire planet if you knew it would happen for certain? What cause do you admire the most?

These are fairly big questions most people never get to consider, until it is too late

What is your true purpose in life? This is the big question everyone who realises they are about to die gets to consider. Did you make a difference? Did you really enjoy your life? Did you have enough fun? Did you love enough? What easy things could you have done to appreciate your life more?

Finding your purpose is something everyone whom I have taken through the dying process has had to address. When the final minutes of life present themselves for contemplation, you will ask yourself "What was the point of my life? What purpose did it serve? On what scale did this happen?"

All too often, when I talk to people at the end of their lives, they get to review what really mattered. At this point, they realise how much time they have spent worrying about details, things and people that appear so irrelevant to them at the end. For most people, petty arguments, hard feelings and squabbles all appear to be utterly futile when death rears its head. Of course, some people choose to hang onto their resentments, bringing them with them to their final moments, and leaving a trail of suffering behind. You can guarantee everyone who does this has never truly considered that they are in this life to make a difference in the world.

Your two ultimate fears

There are two driving forces when it comes to facing your fears that we have already looked at: you are not enough, and you won't be loved. All of your issues in life stem from these two points. Both stem from your relationship with yourself. Can you still love yourself when somebody you love suddenly says they hate or doubt you? Can you still love yourself when you are single? Do you feel you are not significant enough to make a difference in the world? What are you afraid to do that could positively change your life?

Your life map

As with any map, there are two factors that must be in place in order for it to be of any use to you: where you are now and where you want to be. Strangely, most people who have heart attacks know neither. They have been so busy fighting the fires of life, which occur when they don't know where they are or where they are going. Having a map was never considered.

Not having a purpose is like setting out on a journey with no end destination. When you go on holiday, you know where you are going, plan your trip and usually arrive where you intend to be. You do this when you go to work or on a date. Whatever you arrange in your life, you can look up where you are, and where you need to get to. This may seem ridiculously obvious to you as I point this out - because it is.

So, why is it that when it comes to the much bigger and more important journey of life, very few people in the Western world ever consider where they are going until their final hours? Consequently, they drift through life, missing opportunities to be happier and make a bigger difference, and then wonder what happened as they lie, wetting themselves, in a care of the elderly ward. Witnessing this can be a sobering experience.

Have you ever thought where you wanted your lifetime journey to lead?

If you haven't yet thought about this, you will. Maybe this book will be of passing interest, or maybe it will be the electric jolt helping you to put your life back on track, and give your life a little bit more meaning. I have had several years to consider what I felt was missing in my life. Working with people who were about to die is a sobering experience. If you have never given any thought as to the purpose of your life, then you have not yet had a mid-life crisis. I believe these happen when people wake up to their Lunatic Gene, and realise life is too short for monotony, routine and playing it too safe. Eccentricity is born from dancing with The Lunatic Gene. From this place you can have more fun, and laugh at life's lunacy!

Find your purpose

Notice I didn't say: achieve your purpose. Realistically, you know there is a chance this may not happen. However, by finding a purpose that helps you to feel really alive: a purpose which, if you achieved it, would give you more energy and satisfaction than anything you can imagine, a purpose which makes you feel better just by thinking about it, you will energise your entire life. If you even have the thought of achieving your vision, then you have a tool to help you through life's rougher patches. It can also be used to navigate your Emotional Guidance System (EGS).

There are several studies showing how the focus of your thoughts affects your relationships, your health and your life. We will look at some of these in the next chapter.

Chapter 11. Thought Energy

I have said it before and I will say it again; your thoughts are powerful. If you have ever read anything by Louise Hay, Masaru Emoto, Abraham Hicks, Dr Bernie Siegel, Lynne McTaggart, or Dr David Hamilton, you will realise your thoughts can be incredible vehicles of healing or destruction, depending on how you use them. These are a few in a deluge of findings reporting this fact.

Whatever you think about on a moment-to-moment basis has potential ramifications for the rest of your life. This is because you are a creature of habit. If you are currently practising regular, destructive thoughts, then you are hard-wiring a self-destruct course for your heart and life. Conversely, if you are practising gratitude or appreciation regularly and focusing on the magic of life, then you put yourself in an energetic place where healing and happiness are more likely to blossom.

Your thoughts influence your energy, and the entire functioning of your body

Since your body is about 70% water, this section has huge potential ramifications for how your moment-to-moment thoughts have the power to influence at least 70% of your body quickly and directly.

I am going to advocate the work of some incredible people in this section. I will give you a brief overview. If you wish to take any of these areas further, I encourage you to do so. Some of the work I will mention has fascinated me for many hours, throughout many years. Let us start with your body's make up.

Masaru Emoto has proven our thoughts can influence the crystalline structure of water

His journey started when he grew up in Japan, watching a local doctor heal his patients by giving them water. He has spent his life studying water and the effect our thoughts have on it. Through freezing and studying water crystals under a microscope, he has studied the effects that thought had upon them.

He would take a water sample from the same source and study the crystals. Then he would place the water in two separate cups and write on sticky labels 'I love you' and 'You fool', placing one on each sample. A few days later, he would study the crystals from the two samples. The sample with 'You fool' written on it displayed totally distorted crystals. The sample with 'I love you' written on it displayed beautifully synchronised crystals.

This experiment was repeated with water sources from all over the world, with the notes written in many different languages. It did not matter which country, which language or which water source was used; the results were still the same.

The placebo effect is well documented. People who believe something will help them; even if it isn't designed to, will often get the benefits.

More work on this fascinating subject can be found in the work of Dr Fereydoon Batmanghelidj

His experiences of treating illness in an Iranian prison camp are both incredible and inspiring. Being a prisoner himself, he was treating other prisoners' illnesses with nothing but water. He went on to survive, when many didn't, and spent the rest of his life looking into this phenomenon. His life study on this topic led him to believe that up to

80% of all diseases are exacerbated by a direct result of chronic dehydration.

What if your thoughts had the power to heal your body and heart?

I realise this concept may seem a little far-fetched to anyone who has not studied any of the authors I have mentioned in this chapter, or encountered the world of energy medicine. If you are not open to this now, then maybe you will become more open to the possibility when you or one of your family members are handed a death sentence by a well-meaning physician. It is unfortunate, but this is often what it takes for most people to give something like this a chance. It's certainly what it took for me to be open enough to give it a go after studying Western medicine, where drugs solved everything…almost!

As I found out with my experience of Reiki, the power of positive intention to heal oneself is the most remarkable thing you can do for yourself. It breaks my heart when I hear people talk about their terminal diagnoses and give up. If more doctors really embraced the power of positive thought, then more people would live longer. Unfortunately, fear of litigation from potentially grieving family members left behind, is a much more motivating force for many people in the medical establishment. At this stage, for anyone looking for more research or facts into this phenomenon, then I highly recommend the work and books of Dr David Hamilton.

The placebo effect alone is a great reason to embrace positive thought. Dr Hamilton quotes study after study to prove the healing power of your thoughts.

In one of my interviews with Dr Bernie Siegel, author of 'A Book of Miracles', and listed in the top 20 of the Watkins 2011 most spiritually influential people alive, he explained the power of positive thought. He used to be a surgeon and found that, by telling people in-between surgery and their check up to go and do the things they loved, people were living much longer than expected. Having a close call with death, and being encouraged to get pets and/or go out and do the things they loved to do, proved to increase their chances of living a longer, happier life. He mentioned that doctors need to be careful when giving terminal diagnoses, as it can increase the chances of patients dying sooner than is strictly necessary. Hope proves to be a powerful factor in recovery. This is driven by a strong sense of purpose.

When hope is gone, so is life

It is not just the person who is given a terminal diagnosis who suffers – so do all of their family, or at least most of them. For this reason it's a good idea to bear this in mind if you are ever unfortunate enough to find yourself in this position. Ultimately, nobody can escape death, so sometimes it's about finding some sort of inner peace, and leaving as positive a legacy as possible.

The Maharishi effect

The power of positive thought in groups has also been studied. In 1975, Maharishi Mahesh Yogi introduced Transcendental Consciousness to the world. It was a natural extension of Transcendental Meditation, which involved getting a group equivalent of one percent of the population to meditate, stipulating it would have an effect on the entire population. The studies showed an average drop in crime rates of 16% in the cities where the meditations were carried out.

There have been many similar experiments, which prove the power of positive intention. Lynne McTaggart, who wrote 'The Intention Experiment', is continuously looking into this phenomenon, and has found significant changes in behaviour when groups of meditators focus their thoughts. This area is both fascinating and empowering. If you are looking for more information on this area, then I suggest you look up Lynne McTaggart and 'The Intention Experiment'.

Whether you are convinced or not, it is far more likely you will be open to this phenomenon if you, a close friend, or family member, get ill. It is your choice of whether to wait until this happens, or to start opening up to the possibility now. Your thoughts have the power to keep your body, heart and mind in a better state of wellbeing. You also have the power to influence events just by thinking about them.

The attitude of gratitude

There is no question that one of the easiest ways to feel better is to adopt the attitude of gratitude. There is a great healing power when you start to appreciate the people in your life and the things that really work for you.

One of the biggest regrets I used to hear from people at the end of their lives, was they wished they had appreciated their health and youth while they had it. I realise this will not be the most pleasant picture to paint, but I'll do it anyway.

The average person who ends up in the care of the elderly ward will lose control of their bladder and bowels regularly, be unable to walk for any significant distance, and/or have some sort of breathing difficulty. Add the endless hours of sitting in the same place reflecting on what you could, or maybe should, have done differently with your life and how little there is to look forward to. This is a grim place for most, and a distinct possibility for you if you grow old enough to find out.

Of course, this is a grossly generalised picture, but these things happen to many. I have cleaned up enough elderly people to know how difficult it is for them to lose their dignity and hope in such a challenging way. Although their bodies lose control, often their minds do not. Many people who get old will have this to look forward to. For this reason, I recommend if you ever find yourself feeling sorry for yourself and your life, then go to a hospital. When you are there, ask for the care of the elderly ward, and spend some time talking to the patients.

I wonder whether you would dare tell them the things that are troubling you right now. If you do, it is highly likely that you will get a very different perspective on life. When you see what old age has in store, then you are far more likely to feel appreciation for the simple functions in life, like being able to take yourself to the toilet, breathe without equipment or wash yourself. I heard many words of wisdom from my days working with the elderly. Strangely enough, none of them ever wished they had worked more in a job they didn't love, watched more television or done more of what they thought was expected of them by others.

Most people on the elderly ward seemed to regret the same things

Common themes that came up for people at the end of their lives, were the times they wish they had taken a chance, but didn't. The decision to live somewhere else and have a brand new adventure was missed because the judge said no, whilst the jury's verdict was to go. This often leads to a relationship where happiness is compromised, because of the judge overruling the jury: from here it is easy to fall out of love with their lives, their families, and themselves. And this is the last thing many families witness.

Many people had looked forward to doing fun things when they retired, only to have these suddenly taken away when their health went downhill. Time and time again, I would hear the lamentations of elderly patients who had never really understood what their life was about until they had found themselves almost dead. Many people in this position would have gladly sacrificed the rest of their lives for just one hour of being younger and fitter. They have a long time to consider what they would do with such an hour, as they sit for day after day on their bed, wondering why they played it safe and missed out on life's adventure.

Appreciate your health

Just spend a few seconds here to close your eyes, smile and send a big 'thank you' to your body for allowing you the freedom to move and do the things you want it to do. If you repeat this simple exercise regularly, then it is highly likely your body will be healthier as you reach old age. Just being able to stand up and walk, without assistance, is something millions of people would see as incredible.

Some people are blind or deaf. How would you cope if suddenly you couldn't see or hear? Appreciate your sight and your hearing. Be grateful you can breathe, without having to have an oxygen mask wherever you go - as millions of people do.

Appreciate your family

By far the biggest issue I had to deal with when breaking the news of a family death, was the fact people wished they had said certain things when they had the chance. If you love your family and have not told them so for a while, then do it. If you experience the same discomfort as I did, coming from a family who never hugged or used the word 'love', this may be a challenge at first. Indeed, I had to undergo suspicious questioning as my parents attempted to establish what drugs I had taken when I told them, in my thirties, for the first time in almost two decades, that I loved them. However, I can assure you, once you are past the awkwardness, it is a wonderful experience and highly rewarding.

Maybe you feel anger or resentment to one or more of your family members. I do not meet many patients in hospital who did not have an issue with someone in their family. Regardless what they have done to you, remember that thoughts are like boomerangs, and do the most harm to the person thinking them. For this reason, the highest form of revenge is indifference. Better still, the energy of love allows you to learn the lessons of tough situations, say what you need to in order to get it out of your system, and move on with your life.

Telling your family you love them regularly is like buying an insurance policy. You never know when they will die. It is a lot easier to deal with the death of a family member if you know they had known exactly how you felt about them. If your family relationships are more challenging, then you could always write a letter to them. You don't even need to send it. Just the act of writing it will start changing your thoughts towards them. This will reflect in your actions, even if the changes are only subtle.

If you knew today was your last day on this planet, how would you spend it?

If you truly embrace this question, and act upon it in a way that only creates positive effects on yourself, others and the planet, you will get more benefit than any written word, profound statement or inspirational mentor could ever teach.

If you want to use your actions to inspire others, I invite you to contact me and share your story. If it inspires, I will share it with my audience and connect you to a community who could catapult your current life of lunacy into a completely different, and more positive direction.

I am always looking to connect with fellow lunatics and offer you an open door. Whether you decide to walk through it or not will largely depend on your decision whether to fight with your Lunatic Gene, or dance with it. Let go of judgement and guilt, positively change your life and join me in a non-judgemental, guilt-free journey to a happier place.

If you do want to stop fighting your Lunatic Gene and start dancing with it, you will need to connect with the right people and work on your own energy. If you do not yet know who the right people are, I can help you to connect with them, via my social media network, training and events. If you would like access to more tips and get event invites, follow the link to my web site at the end of this chapter and leave your name and email address. Here, you can also find out more about my latest updates, services, and resources to help you to make sense of your life.

"Lunatics of the world unite. You have nothing to lose except your neuroses."

Love,

Adam Shaw

The Heart Guy x

To take this further, find out more about my video training courses at www.thelunaticgene.com/course

About The Author

At the age of seven months Adam was moved into the grounds of a psychiatric hospital, where he lived for the first 17 years of his life. His parents both worked there, and lived within the hospital grounds. Watching people do seemingly insane things has been a large factor in his upbringing. He became a student nurse in 1992, and has worked with people who have health and well being challenges ever since.

The realisation that wellbeing and happiness are both the same thing caused him to follow what made him happy. This journey involved plenty of travel and study into different energy and personal development systems.

His work in counselling those who were facing death has given him a unique perspective on life, and what people regret the most when they are about to die. This has led him to running workshops on happiness, and to travelling to over 30 different countries in 6 different continents, experiencing life to the fullest, having plenty of fun, and some close shaves along the way. Just don't mention swimming with crocodiles, witch doctor parties, or rolling his own car. It pays to be lucky, and happier people appear to be luckier. Adam is the living proof of this so far.

Printed in Great Britain
by Amazon